BUILDINGS AND FACILITIES FOR THE MATHEMATICAL SCIENCES

J. SUTHERLAND FRAME

Professor of Mathematics, Michigan State University

with JOHN W. McLEOD, F.A.I.A.

CONFERENCE BOARD OF

THE MATHEMATICAL SCIENCES

WASHINGTON, D.C. 1963

BUILDINGS AND FACILITIES FOR THE MATHEMATICAL SCIENCES

LIBRARY OF CONGRESS CATALOGUE NUMBER 63-15804

FOREWORD

The physical environment in which mathematicians work is the subject of this book. It was written by a mathematician with the advice of a committee representing mathematics, statistics, and computer science, and drawn from universities, colleges, and high schools. It is intended for those who will design the buildings and who will provide in the next years the library and other teaching and research aids for mathematicians.

The book includes much general information helpful to anyone who must work with an architect in planning an educational building. The book focuses, however, on those special features of design which will most help a mathematician to do his work. Thus the preoccupation with chalkboards and projection equipment would be excessive were it not that communication in the mathematical sciences requires, more than in other fields, visual rather than verbal methods. Similarly, the need for periods of highly concentrated and completely uninterrupted thought, if intricate problems are to be solved or research done, accounts for the strong preference of most mathematicians for individual offices—even, where necessary, at the cost of a size that would be thought uncomfortably confining by those in other disciplines. A corollary of this need for complete privacy and quiet during much of the working day is the desire for public quarters where communication with colleagues can further both professional and personal needs. Hence the need for a "common room" with facilities for serving coffee (*and* furnished with a chalkboard!) is mentioned several times in the book.

Statistical laboratories add an individual feature to plans for housing statistics departments. Special needs for offices suitable for consultation are also noted.

More difficult than the description of recognized desirable features was the attempt to anticipate future developments in teaching methods. Here no firm advice could or should have been given, and the arguments for and against large classes, for example, are presented dispassionately as a contribution to the exercise of wise judgment informed by a knowledge of local conditions.

The rapid development of the field of digital computing makes it especially difficult to properly design buildings for computing centers. This is less because of any prospective change in size of the main computer frame, which already occupies a small part of the total space needed and may even become smaller, than it is because future techniques of handling incoming and outgoing information as well as the numbers and types of users are uncertain. Despite these unknowns, the many buildings that will soon be constructed to house professional computer scientists, their machines, and the occasional user of the machines will be better places in which to work if designed after a study of the relevant sections of this book.

A requirement of this study was that the facilities for teaching mathematics in the secondary schools be included and that this part of the book be publishable as a separate document. If only because of the number of students involved, this part of the study was particularly important. The assistance of those members of the Advisory Committee and other consultants engaged in high school teaching was especially valuable.

The sections of this book written with the advice and assistance of Mr. John W. McLeod, the architect who served as consultant on the project, contain much useful information and wise advice on the steps that must be taken and the cooperation necessary to achieve a well-designed and properly planned building. The mathematician reading this book will be well advised to consider carefully the very different point of view of the architect from his own, and the resultant difficulty in mutual comprehension. If this book communicates the wishes of mathematicians to the architects who will design their buildings, it will have achieved its major purpose.

Professor J. S. Frame of Michigan State University was invited to serve as project director and secured a one-year leave of absence for this purpose. No statement on behalf of the Advisory Committee would be complete without an expression of appreciation to Dr. Frame for his steady and hard work on this project and for the friendly atmosphere of cooperation which has pervaded the meetings of the committee and the innumerable pages of correspondence involved in the work.

This book will contribute to the accumulation of more pleasant working days by thousands of mathematicians in the decades ahead. That many of them will not know of its existence should not diminish the pride felt by Dr. Frame and those who have helped him.

WALLACE GIVENS, Chairman *for the Advisory Committee*

INTRODUCTION

This book contains a synthesis of the ideas of many people concerning the planning and designing of facilities for the mathematical sciences in colleges, universities, and secondary schools. The same ideas may be useful in planning mathematical research centers in industry. The report is intended primarily to serve three groups of people who may become involved in the design of mathematical facilities: mathematicians, architects, and administrators. The term mathematician is to be understood in a broad sense to include all teachers and research workers in pure or applied mathematics, statistics, or computer science.

The Conference Board of the Mathematical Sciences, which sponsored this project to study the design of buildings and facilities for the mathematical sciences, is an organization having the following seven members:

American Mathematical Society
Association for Computing Machinery
Association for Symbolic Logic
Institute of Mathematical Statistics
Mathematical Association of America
National Council of Teaching of Mathematics
Society for Industrial and Applied Mathematics

On July 1, 1960, the recently formed Conference Board opened a Washington office with Dr. G. Baley Price as Executive Secretary. It was clear at this time that there was already a critical shortage of buildings and facilities for departments of mathematics and statistics and for computation centers throughout the United States. Predictions indicated that enrollments in the mathematical sciences would more than double in a decade. It was highly desirable that the Conference Board initiate a project to study the design of buildings and facilities before most of the needed new buildings were planned, in order that the findings might give real assistance to department heads, architects, and administrators involved in the construction of buildings and facilities for the mathematical sciences. The project should consider the needs of secondary schools, as well as those of colleges and universities.[32]

Funds to support this project were provided by a grant of $56,500 from the Educational Facilities Laboratories.[24,64] A subsequent grant subsidized the publication of this report. The first budget included 1) salaries for a mathematician, to serve for one year as director of the project, for his secretary, 2) architectural services, 3) staff travel and travel for delegates to a conference on buildings and facilities, and 4) office rent and supplies. The firm of McLeod and Ferrara, of Washington, D. C., served as architectural consultants. In preparing the sketches and line drawings, Mr. McLeod was ably assisted by Messrs. William Ensign and Richard Passantino. Miss Mary McGugin served capably as secretary for the project, starting in December 1961.

During the year beginning August 1, 1961, the project director visited mathematical facilities (including computation centers) at 43 universities, institutes of technology, colleges, and junior colleges (1 in England; 8, Germany; 2, Denmark; 32, United States), bringing the total number of college and university campuses that he has visited to 120 in the United States and 30 in Canada and Europe. In addition, he visited 19 secondary schools in the United States and 5 in Germany and Denmark. Floor plans were obtained from some of the institutions visited. Some impressions were recorded on tape and polaroid film. Department heads, secretaries, teachers, and school administrators were most generous in showing their facilities, arranging to have professional pictures taken when requested, and contributing their ideas.

Vital to the success of the project was the assistance of the Advisory Committee:

Dr. Wallace Givens, Northwestern University, chairman
Dr. Carl B. Allendoerfer, University of Washington
Mrs. Sarah T. Herriot, Cubberley High School, Palo Alto, California
Dr. Donovan A. Johnson, University of Minnesota
Dr. George E. Nicholson, Jr., University of North Carolina
Dr. Charles E. Rickart, Yale University
Dr. Elbridge P. Vance, Oberlin College

This committee, under the able leadership of Wallace Givens, met in Washington, D. C., on June 16, 1961, with A. W. Tucker, G. B. Price, J. R. Mayor, Jonathan King, and J. S. Frame, to plan the broad outlines of the project and a project questionnaire to be sent out in August to department heads and computation center directors. The committee met again in Washington, December 8–9, 1961, to steer a conference of 34 members, including a distinguished group of speakers and panelists whose names are listed in the appendix. The participants discussed facilities in higher education for administration, instruction, research, and computation in the mathematical sciences, as well as mathematical facilities in the secondary schools. The committee also met on July 9, 1962, to select the photographs and review the drawings, sketches, and manuscript of the semifinal version of the book. Each member gave generously of his time and provided many valuable suggestions for improving both the 25-page summary of the December conference, widely distributed to mathematics departments in January 1962, and the two major preliminary drafts of the book completed April 30 and June 30.

Ideas of the following speakers at the December conference were used extensively in preparing this report: A. W. Calvert, George Grossman, George E. Hay, Magnus Hestenes, Everett Pitcher, Henry Swain, and David M. Young. My grateful appreciation is extended to them and to G. Baley Price, whose guidance and inspiration have had a most important impact on this report.

Special mention should be made of the valuable services of the 1962 Executive Committee of the Conference Board, consisting of A. W. Tucker, chairman, J. B. Rosser, and T. E. Anderson, who nurtured and guided the project, and to John R. Mayor, treasurer, who assisted with the financial arrangements.

To Dr. Harold B. Gores, president of the Educational Facilities Laboratories, Inc., and to Mr. Jonathan King, its secretary, I am pleased to express the gratitude of the entire mathematical community, represented in the Conference Board of the Mathematical Sciences. Their valued advice and financial support made the study possible and provided for the wide distribution of this report.

Finally, thanks are extended to all the hundreds who took time from their busy schedules to answer the questionnaires and supply information for the project.

J. SUTHERLAND FRAME, *Project Director*

TABLE OF CONTENTS

BUILDINGS AND FACILITIES FOR THE MATHEMATICAL SCIENCES

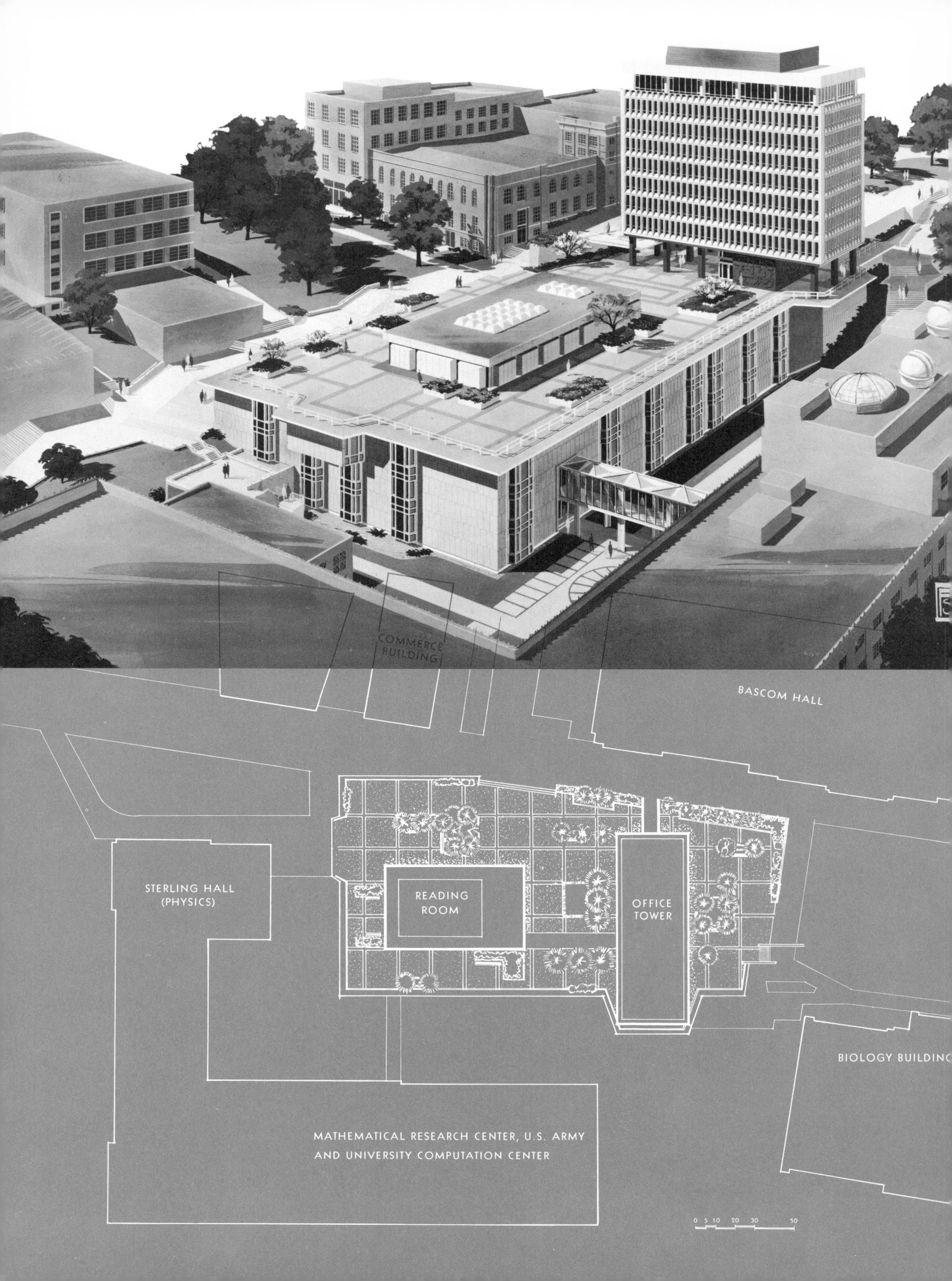
COMMERCE BUILDING
BASCOM HALL
STERLING HALL (PHYSICS)
READING ROOM
OFFICE TOWER
BIOLOGY BUILDING
MATHEMATICAL RESEARCH CENTER, U.S. ARMY AND UNIVERSITY COMPUTATION CENTER
0 5 10 20 30 50

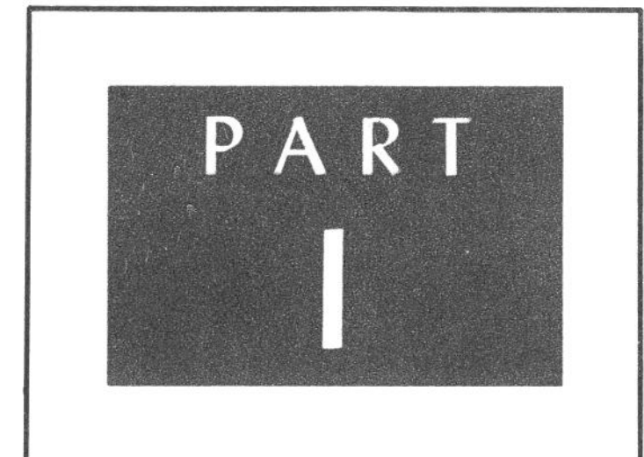

GENERAL CONSIDERATIONS IN THE PLANNING OF FACILITIES

Part One sets the scene for broad concepts in the planning of facilities for the mathematical sciences. The setting includes trends in instruction, job opportunities, student enrollment, teacher shortages, and the findings of the project questionnaire. The basic concepts include assessments of educational responsibilities and space needs, and the roles of the mathematicians, administrators, and architects in the planning process. Part One also gives sample analyses of space needs for the mathematical sciences in small, medium, and large-sized institutions, and appropriate architectural solutions.

Rendering and site plan University of Wisconsin Mathematics Building.

1 THE CHANGING SCENE FOR THE MATHEMATICAL SCIENCES

Mathematics yesterday and today

The mathematical sciences, including mathematics, statistics, computer science, and other related disciplines, are in the midst of an unprecedented period of growth. This growth is reflected in the numbers of people involved, in the extent of the subject matter itself, and in the influence of its thought patterns on society. Facilities for the teaching of mathematics have often been inferior to those available to laboratory science departments; frequently they are antiquated and unsatisfactory. Mathematicians themselves must make a careful study of their needs and then present to the appropriate authorities a well-documented statement of the facilities they will soon need to handle swelling enrollments. The planning of facilities for mathematics cannot await the arrival of a doubled student body. It requires the time and thought of many people. It should be done soon, perhaps now.

Mathematics is one of the oldest subjects in the curriculum. Arithmetic, geometry, and astronomy were high-priority subjects of study for the educated few in the days when Plato, Archimedes, and Euclid were leaders in Greek thought. Geometry was important in the surveying of Egyptian lands flooded annually by the Nile. Calculus, discovered independently and almost simultaneously in the seventeenth century by Newton and Leibnitz, provided a proof (based on Newton's universal law of gravitation) for the laws which Kepler had found to describe the motions of the planets—laws which today are basic in directing the motions of satellites that orbit the earth. A scientific milestone in the early twentieth century was Einstein's theory of relativity, out of which grew the theory and development of nuclear energy.

The publication of mathematical research continues to increase at a prodigious rate. Over 1,000 journals that publish mathematical articles are reviewed in *Mathematical Reviews*. This reviewing journal has grown from 400 pages for the first volume in 1940 and 1,600 pages in 1960 to over 2,400 in 1961 and nearly 2,800 pages in 1962. Library space, conveniently accessible to mathematicians, is sorely needed.

One hundred years ago plane geometry was typically taught in the junior year of college, and trigonometry was considered higher mathematics; today these subjects are being taught in the sophomore or junior year of high school; and in a growing number of schools probability and statistics, or analytic geometry and calculus are being taught to seniors. Sophomore engineering students in college are studying such topics as vector analysis, matrix theory, and numerical analysis, considered graduate mathematics a generation ago. Statistics and computer science are finding an ever-increasing application both in government and in industry. A greater knowledge of mathematics than ever before is needed by the physical and life scientist, the social scientist, and the educated layman.

Interest in mathematics and demand for people trained in mathematics are higher than at any previous period.[8,9,32,44] Mathematics is also a field in which a shortage of trained personnel will continue for the foreseeable future, in high school, college and university teaching as well as in scientific research and development for industry and government.[17,31,61] The federal government has recognized the need to support mathematical research and to train mathematicians in the national interest. Over thirteen million dollars were allocated by the National Science Foundation in grants to summer institutes for mathematics teachers in the year ended June 1961. In the same year additional tens of millions of dollars in research grants and contracts to mathematicians for mathematical research projects were awarded by the National Science Foundation and by the various research agencies of the Department of Defense, including the Office of Naval Research (ONR), the Army Research Office (ARO), and the Air Force Office of Scientific Research (AFOSR). A strong program of teaching and research in mathematics is vital to the scientific development of the country. The need for planning new facilities for mathematics is urgent.

Enrollment trends and job opportunities in the mathematical sciences

The mathematical sciences have been playing an increasingly important role both in the intellectual life of students and teachers in our schools, colleges, and universities, and in the world of industry and government. Greatly increased job opportunities in these fields have stimulated a marked increase in the number of students enrolling in mathematics at all levels as well as in the number choosing mathematics as a major.[44] High schools record increased enrollments in junior and senior mathematics courses,[6] and many have embarked on programs of enrichment or advanced placement for senior students who have already completed as juniors the work of the traditional senior high school mathematics course. The increasing awareness of the importance of mathematics not only in the physical and life sciences, but in the social sciences as well, has caused enrollments in mathematics to increase at a much more rapid rate than total enrollments in schools and colleges, and these college enrollments are expected to nearly double in 10 years![61,62]

At the college level the 2.24 ratio of increase in the number of bachelor's degrees in mathematics awarded by all U. S. colleges and universities—from 4,034 in 1955 to 9,019 in 1959—was the greatest ratio of increase recorded in any field of study.[30] An additional 27 per cent increase to 11,437 was recorded in 1960, and the estimate for 1962 was about 15,000. Many institutions recorded at least a tripling in the number of majors in the mathematical sciences between 1955 and 1960, possibly in part because the various new mathematics curricula in high schools may equip more students to enter college better prepared in mathematics and more favorably disposed to continue the subject. A further increase in college enrollments in mathematics and statistics by a factor between 2 and 3 appears likely in the decade 1960–1970. In Table 1 are shown the number of degrees granted in mathematics and statistics in the United States for the years 1948 to 1961 at the bachelor's, master's, and Ph.D. levels. Increases in the number of graduate degrees show an understandable time lag of one year from bachelor's degree to master's degree, and of three or even considerably more years from master's degree to Ph.D. The big bulge in graduate study has already begun. As a result of increasing enrollments and increasing emphasis on mathematics, statistics, and computer science, many additional buildings and facilities must be constructed for the mathematical sciences in the next decade.

Despite increasing enrollments, the supply of capable men and women trained in mathematics and statistics has not kept pace with the demand. The rapid increase in automation involving the use of digital computers has created surpluses of certain types of unskilled labor, but it has created a higher demand for people with training and skill in the mathematical sciences. Our national survival in the new space age has become increasingly dependent on the solution of scientific problems involving a high level of mathematics. Mathematicians are needed at the bachelor's level and more especially at the higher levels.[62] A study of the long-range demand for scientific and technical personnel, conducted for the National Science Foundation by the Bureau of Labor Statistics of the U.S. Department of Labor, indicated a projected increase in the scientific and engineering employment of mathematicians from 29,000 in 1959 to 60,000 in 1970 (Fig. 1).[31] This increase of 107 per cent was a higher percentage increase than that of any of the other sciences, although the increase in absolute numbers was larger in some other fields. If this projected need is to be met, improved efficiency in the education of mathematicians is essential.

Predicted teacher shortage and its implications for building needs

The increased demand for mathematicians and statisticians in industry and government, coupled with growing enrollments, has produced a marked shortage of teachers in these fields in high schools, colleges, and universities. The 1961 Higher Education Research Report of the National Education Association[61] recorded that out of 1,085 institutions of higher education that replied, 525 foresaw more acute shortage of qualified candidates for teaching positions in mathematics, and 492 in the physical sciences, but less than half this number in any other discipline. It seems likely that by 1970 the number of qualified teachers for the mathematical sciences in colleges and universities may be only 25 to 50 per cent greater than in 1960; and that these teachers may have to teach mathematics to between two and three times as many students in 1970 as were enrolled in 1960. Similar indications of shortages of high school mathematics teachers will be discussed in Part III (p. 113). The current and impending teacher shortage in mathematics has implications not only for new methods of teaching, but also

TABLE 1 *Number of Degrees Conferred Annually in Mathematics and Statistics* by Level of Degrees*[30]

Year ending June 30	*Number of degrees conferred*			*Per cent† of all degrees conferred*		
	Bachelor's	*Master's*	*Doctor's*	*Bachelor's*	*Master's*	*Doctor's*
1948	4,266	711	128	1.56	1.68	3.21
1949	5,040	893	126	1.37	1.76	2.50
1950	6,392	974	160	1.47	1.67	2.41
1951	5,753	1,109	184	1.49	1.70	2.51
1952	4,721	802	206	1.42	1.26	2.68
1953	4,396	677	241	1.44	1.11	2.90
1954	4,090	706	227	1.40	1.24	2.52
1955	4,034	761	250	1.40	1.31	2.83
1956	4,660	898	235	1.50	1.51	2.64
1957	5,546	965	249	1.63	1.56	2.84
1958	6,924	1,234	247	1.89	1.88	2.76
1959	9,019	1,499	282	2.34	2.16	3.01
1960	11,437	1,765	303	2.90	2.27	3.09
1961	13,137	2,338	344	3.27	2.97	3.25

* Includes actuarial science.

† Per cent at bachelor's level is based upon all bachelor's and first-professional degrees conferred that year. First-professional degrees are not included in columns for master's and doctor's degrees.

for the design of new facilities, both in colleges and in high schools. Teaching certain parts of mathematics to groups larger than the conventional class of 20 to 35 may soon be a necessity in many colleges and high schools. Some are already using either big lecture sections or television to instruct a large number of students with a limited number of qualified teachers. Many institutions in the near future will need new buildings that make adequate provision for the teaching of mathematics to large groups and yet afford opportunities for personal contact between students and faculty.

Good facilities also play their part in attracting competent personnel. Mathematics has not been one of the well-housed departments in most colleges and universities. Too often mathematics or statistics is simply assigned space that became available when some laboratory science department moved into a new building; this space may or may not provide suitable facilities. Well-planned mathematical facilities have always been important, but because of the existing teacher shortage it will be increasingly important for institutions to have good facilities to attract qualified mathematicians and statisticians to their campuses.

FIGURE 1 *Percent change in scientific and engineering employment for the entire civilian economy, by occupation, 1959 to projected 1970*[31]

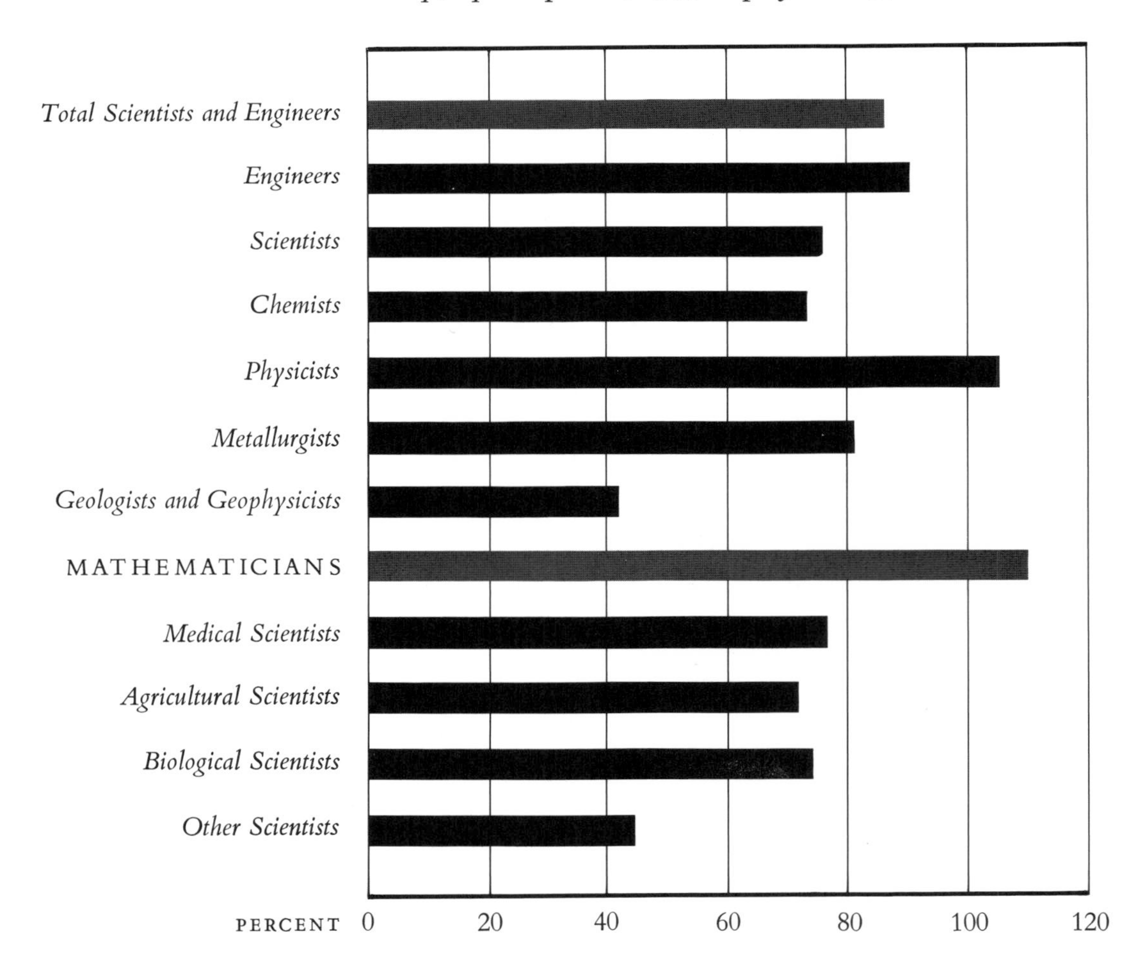

TABLE 2 *Number of Institutions Expecting Various Percentage Increases in Mathematics Enrollment from 1960 to 1965*

Expected increase in mathematics enrollment (by percentages)	*Number of institutions grouped by mathematics enrollment*				*Per cent of total institutions*
	Small 1–500	*Medium 501–1,500*	*Large 1,501–8,300*	*Total*	
0–19	21	14	10	45	18.3
20–39	33	27	30	90	36.6
40–59	23	17	10	50	20.3
60–79	8	8	9	25	10.2
80–99	3	6	5	14	5.7
100+	15	6	1	22	8.9
	103	78	65	246	100.0

The project questionnaire: planned new construction

To obtain information about existing facilities for the mathematical sciences in colleges and universities, and expectations of enrollment growth and building plans, a project questionnaire was mailed in August–September 1961. Replies were received from 300 of the 620 mathematics and statistics departments and from 65 of the 90 computer centers to which the questionnaire was sent. Some replies were incomplete.

One question concerned plans for new facilities. Replies showed that 6 per cent of the mathematics and statistics departments reporting were moving into new quarters in 1961, and an additional 39 per cent had at least tentative plans for additional buildings or facilities by 1965. Similarly, the replies showed that 40 per cent of the 65 computer center directors reporting expected new facilities between 1961 and 1965 (3 per cent in 1961), although many were in relatively new installations already. Over 150 colleges and universities in the United States and Canada had high-speed digital computer installations in the fall of 1961.[21] An expected doubling of this number by 1965 will involve the building of many new facilities for computer science.

Another question concerned the expected increase in enrollments in mathematics courses between fall 1960 and fall 1965. The 246 institutions answering this question are classified in Table 2 as small, medium-sized, or large, according to their 1960 mathematics enrollment. It will be noticed that almost half of the institutions expect their mathematics enrollments to increase by at least 40 per cent in the five-year period. Two five-year increases of 41 per cent would produce a doubling in ten years at these institutions. An additional increase in the total mathematics enrollment in the country is to be expected from newly formed colleges and junior colleges.

Information was obtained from the questionnaire about the size of classes at various institutions. Among 284 mathematics and statistics departments replying to this question, 100 reported having classes of more than 40 but not more than 100 students, and an additional 33 reported having large classes in excess of 100, a few of them with nearly a fifth of their teaching hours being so handled. Thus it appears that increasing enrollments have already forced many mathematics departments to experiment with classes larger than the traditional 20 to 30.

A subsequent postcard questionnaire was sent in May 1962 to 100 institutions that reported having departmental libraries for mathematics or shared branch libraries. Information from these replies will be discussed in the section on libraries (pp. 84-85).

The mathematical research laboratory in industry

Facilities for mathematicians and statisticians are needed not only in academic institutions but in the research laboratories of industry and government (Fig. 2)[17] where considerable numbers of these people are employed. Although college mathematics through calculus and differential equations were used to a considerable extent in solving industrial problems in the decade following World War II, the men who used this mathematics were usually trained or at least classified as engineers or physicists rather than as mathematicians. Prior to 1950, very few industrial scientists were employed primarily as mathematicians. Recently, the rapidly expanding fields of electronic computation, industrial research, and space technology have given the mathematician an important and recognized place in research sponsored by industry and government.

There were 66 industrial and government establishments employing in a given place 10 or more persons whose names were included in the 1960–61 combined membership list of the American Mathematical Society, the Mathematical Association of America, and the Society for Industrial and Applied Mathematics.[44] About one-third of the membership of these organizations is now in nonacademic employment. Many mathematicians and statisticians who are not members of the American Mathematical Society are employed in computation centers. Industry could easily absorb several hundred new mathematics and statistics Ph.D.'s each year, but the total number receiving the Ph.D. in mathematics or statistics in the United States in 1961 was only 367. (See also Table 1, for academic year ending June 30.)

Many industrial research organizations are taking an active part in trying to increase the supply of Ph.D.'s in mathematics and statistics, either by giving financial support for their employees' education or by arranging to have advanced courses in mathematics taught on company time and in company buildings (Fig. 3). A still larger number of industrial organizations use mathematicians in their computation centers (Fig. 4). Thus the problem of adequate facilities for teaching and research in mathematics, statistics, and electronic computation is not restricted to academic institutions.

---

2 INSTRUCTION IN THE MATHEMATICAL SCIENCES

Relationship of mathematics to the overall educational program

Whenever there is some freedom of choice in the location of a mathematics, statistics, or computing facility, it is wise to take into account the relationships of these subjects to the overall educational program. In a small school the mathematics teacher may also teach one of the sciences. Obviously, it is advantageous that his mathematics classrooms be near his classrooms and laboratories in the other sciences. In a larger school it may be

FIGURES 2, 3, 4

Mathematician's office, Boeing Scientific Research Laboratories, Seattle, Washington

Classroom used for mathematics, Boeing Scientific Research Laboratories

Computation Center, Aerospace Corporation, El Segundo, California

3

4

possible to have a separate floor or separate wing, or possibly even a separate building, either for mathematics alone or for mathematics and science (Fig. 5).

Any use of a joint facility such as a mathematics and science library presupposes that the departments involved have nearby facilities. On a college campus too small to support a separate library for mathematics, it would be desirable to house mathematics, statistics, physics, and astronomy in the same building with a common library, and to have the computation center either in the same building or close by.

The problem of student traffic between classes should also be considered, especially on a large campus. Students in the physical sciences and engineering may be required to take mathematics for two to four years and statistics for one or two semesters in college. Students in business administration, economics and other social sciences, biological sciences, and other disciplines may be required to take one or two years of mathematics and statistics in college, or to make up a mathematical deficiency without full credit in graduate school. Classes to be taken by the same students should if possible be scheduled in rooms near enough to each other that the distance between them can be walked in the allotted interval between classes.

If one year of college mathematics is required of a large percentage of the student body, then either the mathematics classrooms should be centrally located on the campus, or some freshman sections might be taught in classrooms that are suitably furnished for mathematics instruction but are not housed with the mathematics department.[54] As an experiment to alleviate student traffic between classes, Michigan State University has built some dormitories for freshmen that contain a number of classrooms suitable for certain required freshman courses. Residents of these dormitories would normally attend only classes offered in the dormitory during one-half of each day, and classes offered elsewhere on campus during the other half days. Clearly, if such dormitory classrooms are to be used for instruction in mathematics, they should have the chalkboards and other facilities required for a mathematics classroom.

Teaching of mathematics in the schools

Since the design of facilities for mathematics in the high schools will be discussed at length in Part III, we shall confine our remarks here to some general considerations. Good curriculum planning should precede facilities planning. Facilities for mathematics depend to a large degree on how mathematics is to be taught, and methods vary from school to school and among teachers in the same school. Three aspects of teaching methods have especially important implications for building design: 1) the size of classes, 2) the manner of presenting visual materials to the class, and 3) the types of learning activities for students other than watching and listening to class presentations by a teacher. In some schools each teacher may meet regularly with a class of 20 to 35 students and teach an entire course without the aid of other teachers. In other schools instruction in a single course may be shared by two or more teachers. Possibly some of the material will be presented to two or more classes at once, either in a double room, divisible by a folding partition into two separate classrooms (Fig. 27), in a large lecture room, or on television; and other parts of the course may be learned in small groups or even at individual stations with teaching machines.

In presenting materials to a class, one teacher may rely heavily on writing classroom notes and problems on the front chalkboard, but seldom require students to do work at the board; for him a large front board is essential and boards on other walls are of minor importance. Another teacher may wish to have as many of his students as pos-

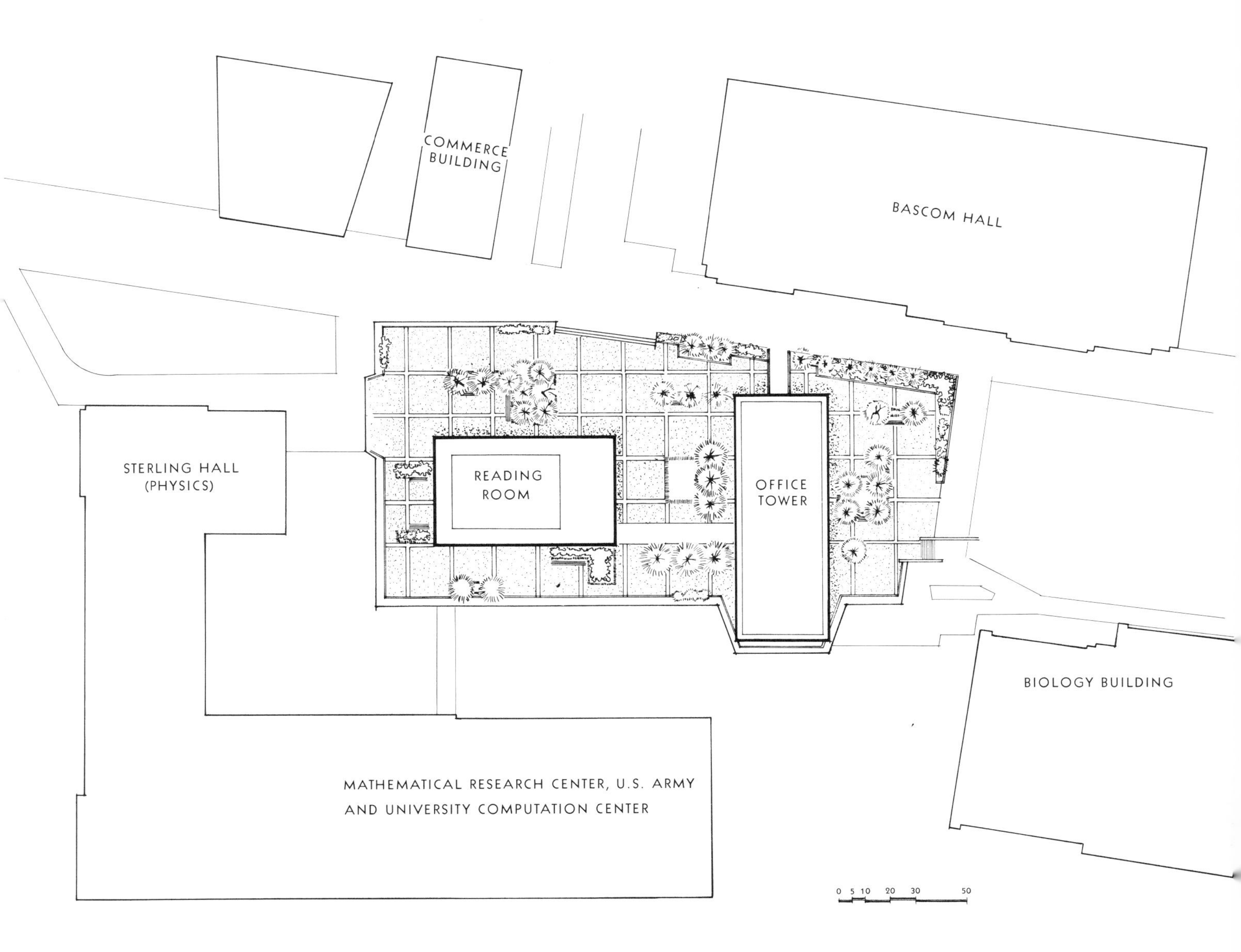

FIGURE 5 *Site plan, University of Wisconsin Mathematics Building*

sible work at the board at once; for him, even three walls lined with chalkboard may seem insufficient. One teacher may find the overhead projector a very convenient way to present material to the class (Fig. 50), whereas another would not use the machine even if it were installed and available. Some teachers may wish to make occasional use of filmstrips and movies; others will not. Some mathematics departments may wish to use television for some of the instruction; others will not.

Some elementary and secondary teachers may feel that calculating machines are an effective device for teaching students to understand our numerative system with its decimal notation; some teachers may wish their students to know how to use calculating machines for arithmetical computations; both groups may feel that a room equipped with desk calculators is important (Fig. 25). Other teachers may be either lukewarm or averse to the use of calculators by their students. Some mathematics teachers may wish to have students work with measuring instruments and do experiments in geometry leading to the discovery of important theorems, like the Pythagorean theorem in the plane or in space. They will want a mathematics laboratory equipped for such individualized learning activities (Fig. 54).

Other mathematics teachers may feel that for most students such activity is relatively unimportant.

Clearly, the methods for presenting mathematics must be carefully examined before the requirements of the new facility can be stated. The difficulty is that teachers will change and teaching methods may change, but the building remains. Whenever possible, therefore, the building should be designed not only with the present teaching methods in mind, but with a thought of what the future may hold. Electrical outlets and television conduits should not be overlooked in the initial plans, even if they may not be needed immediately. Ample facilities for visual aids must also be considered before the building is built. Rooms to be shared with other sciences may need outlets for gas, as well as for water and electricity.

Mathematical instruction in universities in the United States and Europe

The teacher of a course in mathematics or statistics in a college or university is usually expected to organize a certain segment of mathematical knowledge, with or without the aid of textbooks; present it lucidly to a class; and stimulate the individual students to understand the material, think creatively about it, and possibly use it in doing assigned work. In the United States, the teacher is also expected at regular intervals to assign grades that measure each student's mastery of the subject. Grades may be based entirely on written homework, reports, and examinations, or they may take oral work into account.

The pattern of instruction in the mathematical sciences is likely to involve more physical activity on the part of the teacher than in the social sciences or humanities. Seldom does a mathematician who is not physically handicapped sit down to give a lecture or read his lecture verbatim from a set of notes. Typically, he walks back and forth in front of the chalkboard and writes as he talks. If he must use a microphone while writing on a chalkboard, he would prefer one of the new radio type that permits greater freedom of movement. Better yet, he would prefer a lecture room with such good acoustics that a microphone is not needed.

Many college mathematics teachers feel that personal contact between teacher and student is very important for effective teaching. Some call on individual students frequently by name and ask them to recite in class. Some achieve personal contact in a small class by sending all the students to the board to do problems. The chief objection to the use of large lecture sections or television for instruction in mathematics is the difficulty of achieving personal contact between student and instructor. Hence the size of most mathematics classes in the United States has been limited to 20–30 students or less. Enrollment pressures are now changing this pattern and may do so more decisively. When large lecture sections are used, they may be varied to permit greater student participation by dividing the large lecture section into small recitation sections once or twice a week, taught either by the lecturer himself or by his assistants.

Division of a single course into small parallel sections is generally avoided in European countries. Common practice in Germany and Denmark, for example, is to schedule only one section in a course, unless enrollment exceeds the capacity of the available lecture hall. Thus elementary classes may be taught to 100 or even as many as 500 or 750 students, whereas advanced seminars are usually conducted in small groups.

New buildings planned at the Johannes Gutenberg University in Mainz, Germany, include an equilateral triangular building housing three auditoriums suitable for mathematics classes of 260, 198, and 198 students, respectively, with a common lobby at the center of the building per-

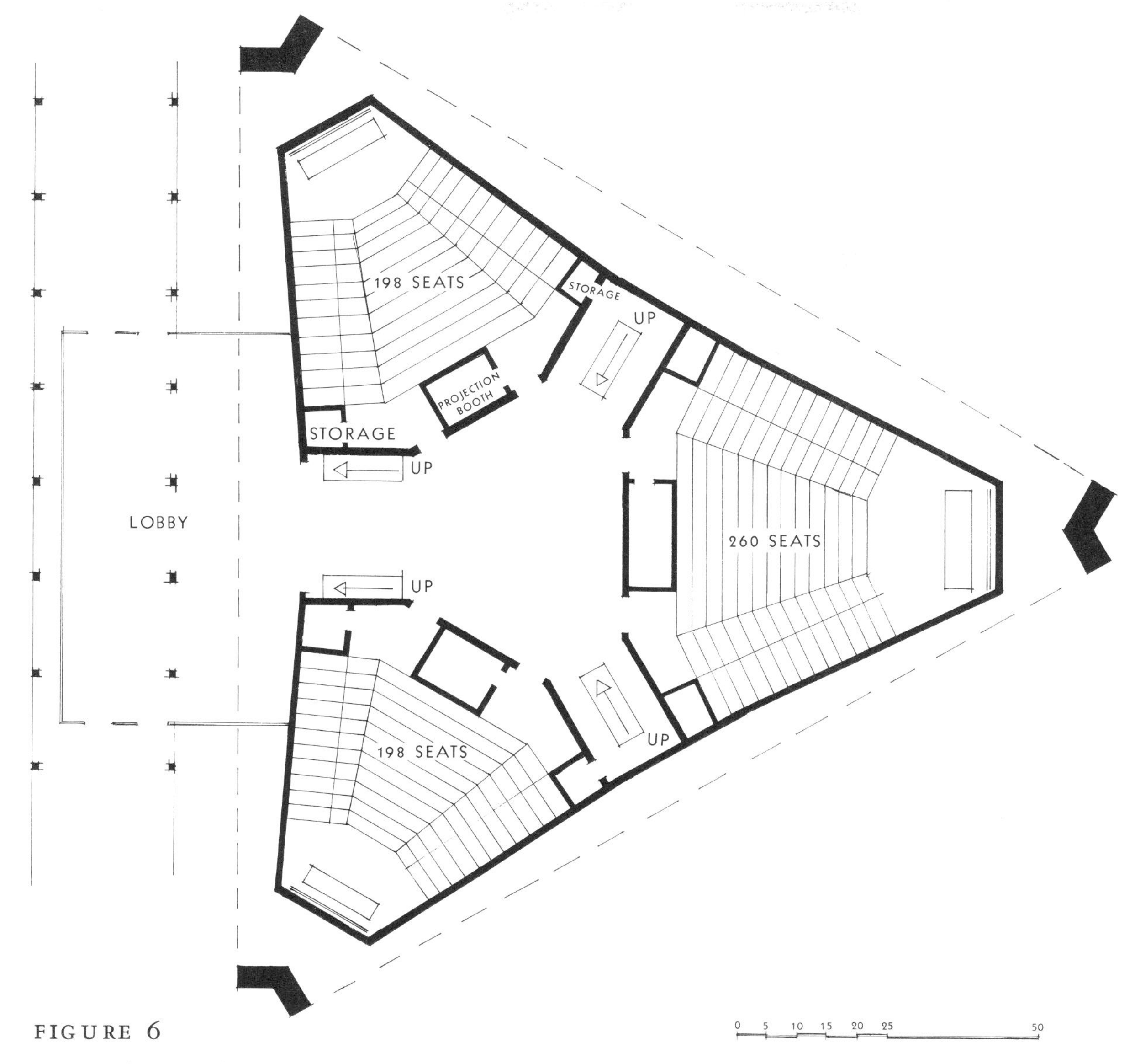

FIGURE 6

Proposed triangular auditorium building, Johannes Gutenberg Universität, Mainz, Germany

mitting easy passage from one lecture room to the next (Fig. 6).

Lectures to a very large class usually require visual amplification by an overhead projector, and acoustical amplification by a microphone and a loudspeaker system. However, if the lecture hall has good acoustics, a lecturer with a resonant speaking voice may be heard well by a class of 200 to 300 or even more.

If the number of qualified and available mathematics teachers does not increase as rapidly as mathematics enrollments, it will probably be necessary for many colleges and universities in the United States to make greater use of either large lecture sections or television for teaching mathematics courses with big enrollments.

Both in the United States and abroad, advanced seminars in mathematics are generally taught in an atmosphere that encourages active student participation. At this level one of the prime goals is to stimulate the student into independent creative activity.

In the teaching of certain courses in statistics and numerical analysis, an important role is played by computation that is sufficiently complicated to require the use of electric desk calculators. For this purpose, a room should be provided in which students can obtain group instruction in the use of desk calculators and also use them individually outside of class for their computations (Fig. 25). Since expensive equipment is involved, the room should be supervised, possibly by a secretary or nonstaff member having an adjacent office (Figs. 7b, 8a, 10b). When the statistics department and computation center are close together, there is an advantage in having a statistical laboratory easily accessible to both groups. High speed computation likewise plays an important role in the study of computer science and numerical analysis. The electronic computers required to solve the assigned problems now operate at speeds close to a million times as fast as a desk calculator, but the writing and grading of programs are so time-consuming that efforts, as yet only partly successful, are being made to have the computer take over at least part of this work.

Changing techniques in mathematical instruction

In recent years a number of relatively new techniques have been tried for the teaching of mathematics involving such things as overhead projectors and other visual aids, television, programed instruction, and teaching machines. These will be discussed at greater length in Part IV. While it is not expected that any one school will adopt all these new techniques within a decade, it is certain that some of them are bound to be tried by many institutions before the buildings built in this decade are demolished. Building plans must certainly take these possibilities into account. One aid to mathematics instruction that has already found official acceptance by national mathematics organizations at their meetings is the overhead projector (see p. 141).

The television medium, either by distant broadcasts or by coaxial cable within an institution, provides a means for bringing a teacher before a large audience. It has been tried successfully in the national broadcast of the "Continental Classroom" courses, "Modern Algebra," and "Probability and Statistics" (see p. 147). It has also been used by some schools and colleges to bring several sections of one course together for a common presentation of part of the subject matter. In some schools a substantial portion of the mathematical instruction is presented by television (p. 148). Some mathematics teachers have been enthusiastic about television instruction, while others have been lukewarm or antagonistic. Like the overhead projector, the television screen displays only a small field of vision to be viewed at one time. Both devices provide magnification, which permits small objects to be seen clearly by a group. The size of the audience that can be reached by television is almost limitless, but the audience receives the information without active participation in the form of questions or discussion. To offset this disadvantage, television offers the possibility of having a taped lecture repeated at several hours in the day. This creates greater flexibility in scheduling and permits slower students to view the material more than once. Television instruction in mathematics will be discussed at greater length in Part IV.

Another technique which may influence mathematics teaching is that of programed instruction and teaching machines.[51] The idea of programed instruction is to present a body of knowledge to students individually in a sequence of small steps followed by questions which the student is called upon to answer before proceeding. The programed instruction may be presented in printed form, calling for responses before turning the page; or it may be presented by teaching machines of various degrees of complexity, requiring electrical connections and specially designed rooms (see p. 149). Enthusiasts for the new machines feel that they may be able to supplant in large degree our present methods of instruction. Others feel that these machines may well have a place in presenting factual information, or in assisting students who have missed class because of illness, but that they can never provide the stimulation and inspiration that a good teacher can impart to his class.

Another way in which machinery has been used to reduce the drudgery of teaching is in connection with the correcting and grading of programs prepared by students learning to program a computer. A program consists of a large number of individual instructions which tell the machine to perform certain arithmetical operations in order to obtain the answer to a more or less complicated problem. Seldom does a student write a correct program on the first attempt. The process called "debugging" is used to try to find errors in the program and correct them. Individual grading of such programs may be so time-consuming that large classes cannot be handled by a single instructor without assistance. However, some computer specialists have devised super programs that enable the machine itself to print out information telling the student at what point he went wrong, and also to count the number of times the student needed prompting in order to achieve a correct program. The student's grade depends in part on the number of trial runs before achieving the correct program.

Searching the literature is an important activity in advanced mathematical research that should be learned and practiced at the undergraduate level. Computers are playing a significant role in information retrieval, which already has important implications for libraries. In the past the contents of a book have been summarized on one or two library cards stating not much more than the author's name and the title. To learn which books or journals contain information on a specific topic of immediate interest to the reader, it has been necessary to browse through many volumes in the library stacks. Using computers with magnetic tape memory and appropriate codes for key words, it is possible to evoke and print out references to particular pages of a long list of books and journals that contain pertinent information on a given subject—provided, of course, that this information has been previously encoded.

New techniques in mathematical instruction may have their impact on building design. Both the size and shape of the spaces needed for instruction by these techniques, and also the electrical and other facilities required, must be considered in designing a new mathematics building.

---

3 BASIC CONSIDERATIONS IN PLANNING MATHEMATICS FACILITIES

Assessing the educational responsibilities of the department

Before any details of new facilities for a department of mathematics or statistics or a computing center are worked out, the department should be prepared to answer three important questions. Why do we need new facilities? What new facilities do we need? Where should these facilities be located? The "why" and "what" can be answered only after a careful assessment of the educational responsibilities of the department. The "where" involves the overall relationships of the department to others in the development of the campus site.

The educational responsibilities of a mathematics department will probably include the teaching of courses to a rapidly increasing number of majors and nonmajors, and possibly to community groups in adult education. These responsibilities may include an active research program in mathematics involving graduate students and staff members on contract research; graduate students who are supported by fellowships or teaching assistantships; and faculty members who pursue their research without substantial reduction in teaching load. The mathematics department may be concerned with visiting scholars who spend a term or a year at the institution in a teaching or research capacity; summer institute or academic-year institute programs for special groups; radio or television broadcasting of mathematical programs; holding occasional or frequent meetings of regional or national groups of mathematicians on campus.

A separate statistics department may also have similar duties. Whether separate or combined with mathematics, a statistics faculty is called upon for a considerable amount of consulting with faculty and students of other departments. It may also have the responsibility for a statistical laboratory equipped with desk calculators. Both staff time and appropriate space must be provided for these activities.

A computation center has a somewhat different area of responsibility. Although large groups may be taught the fundamentals of computer programing and numerical analysis, the major duties of the staff involve research and individual consultation rather than group teaching. Conference rooms and program preparation areas generally require more space than classrooms in a computation center. This is particularly true at present because limited staffs in computing centers and the newness of the field, together with the resulting lack of suitable textbooks and teaching techniques, force each faculty member and student to come to the center to get his problem done; each must learn how to use the computer to a considerable extent by self-study and experimentation. Thus, the saturation of use of even a very large computer by research computations is frequently encountered. It is expected that many people will require laboratory experience with a computer. A small computer accessible to students may be considered desirable for instructional purposes in a center where a large, fast machine is tightly scheduled. If so, space for this machine will be needed. On the other hand, a small machine will impose limitations, particularly on machine-aided coding techniques such as the use of automatic programing languages. Furthermore, the cost per unit operation decreases as the capability of the machine increases. Hence, various efforts are being made to improve the accessibility to students of the large, fast computers, so that many students may learn their use by actually running examples on them. How this accessibility will be achieved in the future is not now clear, but already a few universities with well-staffed computation centers are making the fast computer available to large groups of students for instructional purposes. Working space for these students should not be overlooked.

Instructional responsibilities are usually a major factor in the space needs for mathematics. In planning a building or facility these responsibilities should be considered not only for the present, or for the date the building is to be completed, but for at least five or ten years beyond the completion date. Too often a new facility proves to be inadequate from the start, because no provision was made for growth, or because the rate of growth was underestimated. For the purposes of our discussion, let us call the date when the new facility is expected to be unable to provide for further growth without expansion or remodeling the *saturation* date.

Stage one in the departmental inventory of space needs concerns the estimated need for classroom space. First it is necessary to assume a saturation date, estimate course enrollments in mathematics and statistics at various levels for this saturation date, and decide whether these students are to be taught in standard-sized classes (under 36), in medium-sized classes (36–100), in large lecture sections (over 100), or by television. If large lecture sections are to be used for part of the instruction, it must be decided whether or not each large section should be broken up on certain days of the week into small discussion sections. From these decisions and assumptions is derived the total estimated number of lecture sections, recitation sections, standard- and medium-sized classes, for various levels of instruction. The next assumption to be made involves classroom use—more specifically, the number of hours per day and the number of days per week that a given classroom is to be used. There are wide differences between institutions on this point.[29,34,55] At some it is difficult to get students to elect a class after 3 p.m., while at some large city institutions the early evening hour is the most crowded in the day. However, it should be possible to make a rational estimate of classroom needs based on the use that is considered acceptable for one's own institution. It is better not to have all classrooms of equal size, since it may be necessary at the last minute to accommodate a few extra students in two or three courses without creating extra sections. Stage one in the study of space needs is completed with an estimate of the number of classrooms and lecture rooms of each size that will be needed by the department at the saturation date, some possibly to be shared with other departments. Itemize:

1 Number and sizes of classrooms.
2 Number and sizes of lecture halls.

Stage two in the inventory concerns other spaces needed for instruction, which may include the following:

1 A departmental library, possibly shared with other departments.
2 A general study room where students may work between classes on assignments that do not ininvolve the use of the library.
3 One or more conference rooms or seminar rooms.
4 A common room or lounge, with adjoining kitchenette, to serve as a center for the exchange of ideas on an informal basis; and a colloquium room adjacent to or combined with the lounge, to be used for special lectures by invited speakers or staff members. (A separate colloquium room may also double as a classroom.)
5 One or more rooms equipped with desk calculators.
6 A small computation center to be used mainly for instructional purposes.

Stage three involves a study of office space, one of the major requirements of a mathematics department. Adequate and appropriate space is needed both for the departmental administrative headquarters and for offices of regular teachers, temporary and part-time teachers, staff members and visitors on research, and teaching assistants, fellows, and graduate students.

To estimate the requirements of office space for the teaching staff, an assumption must be made about appropriate teaching loads for various staff members, in view of their rank, their research activities, their administrative responsibilities in the department, and any time-consuming responsibilities with national organizations. An estimate is first made of the size of the staff at various levels (graduate assistants, instructors, senior staff) required to teach the estimated number of classes at the saturation date. To this teaching-staff estimate must be added the number of regular staff and assistants assigned to research (with appropriate allowance for those engaged in both research and teaching), and the number of secretaries for whom office space should be provided. Secretarial assistance is needed not only for the administrative headquarters, but also to assist staff members in preparing materials for distribution to their classes and in preparing articles for publication in scientific journals.

Offices of various sizes should be provided, and whenever possible these should be private offices.

Details of the need for private offices and of the requirements for the department headquarters will be discussed in subsequent sections.

Sample analyses of space needs and architectural solutions

SPACE ESTIMATES To illustrate these ideas, let us examine in some detail three possible analyses of space needs in planning a new facility for the mathematical sciences, one for a small college, one for a medium-sized institution, and a third for a large university. Figures given below are for illustration only and are not intended to imply an opinion regarding proper teaching loads or class sizes. Planning is being started now, we assume, for a facility with completion date three or four years hence, and a saturation date ten years hence. A doubling of the present mathematics enrollment is expected by the saturation date.

Having determined the spaces needed in the proposed facility for the educational program, and having assigned to each the appropriate area in square feet, a first subtotal called "usable space" or "assignable space" is obtained.[27] To this must be added a subtotal for large auxiliary service areas, such as boiler plants, mechanical rooms, toilets, elevators, custodial space, etc. Then to the combined total area for educational and supporting services must be added an area, usually estimated as an additional 25 per cent, for corridors and stairhalls. This estimate is in accord with the findings of a study of instructional buildings in the United States that about 20 per cent of the gross area was used by corridors (1/6) and stairhalls (1/30).[25,62] Toilets, custodial space, and circulation areas together occupy an estimated 25 per cent of the gross area.

FACILITY FOR A SMALL COLLEGE The present mathematics staff of three, teaching 200 students enrolled in mathematics courses, includes a chairman, teaching less than a full load, and two full-time teachers, but no one assigned to research. It is anticipated that, at the saturation date ten years hence, a student enrollment of 400 in mathematics and statistics, totaling about 1,460 student credit hours, will be divided into classes as shown in the table at the foot of this page. Teachers A and B are the department chairman and associate chairman, each teaching part time. An additional teacher G would be assigned to full-time research,

Course level	*Total enrollment*	*Course credit hours**	*Number of sections*	*Number of students per section*	*Student credit hours*	*Number of hours taught by* A	B	C	D	E	F
Freshman	210	4 { 3 L	1	100	300			3			
		1 R	(5)	(20 each)	100		1	2	2		
		4	2	35,25	240				4		4
		3	2	25,25	150					3	3
Sophomore	90	4	1	40	160		4				
		3	2	25,25	150					3	3
Junior and Senior	100	4	2	35,25	240	4				4	
		3	2	15,25	120			3	3		
	400		12+(5)		1,460	4	5	8	9	10	10

* Combined lecture and recitation except lecture (L) or recitation (R) as shown.

or the research assignment might be shared with one or two other staff members in exchange for part of their teaching assignments.

Space needs for a floor for the mathematical sciences (partly shared with others) fall into the following categories (Figs. 7a, b):

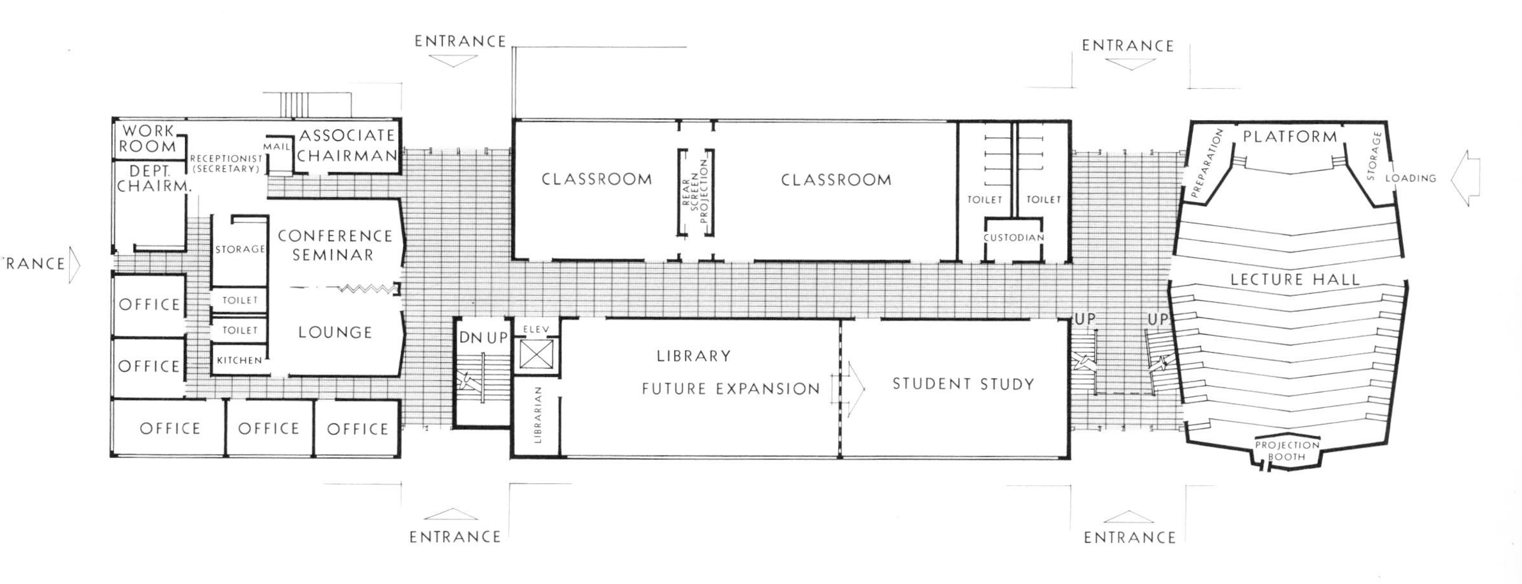

FIGURE 7 A *The mathematics floor of a science-mathematics building in a small college*

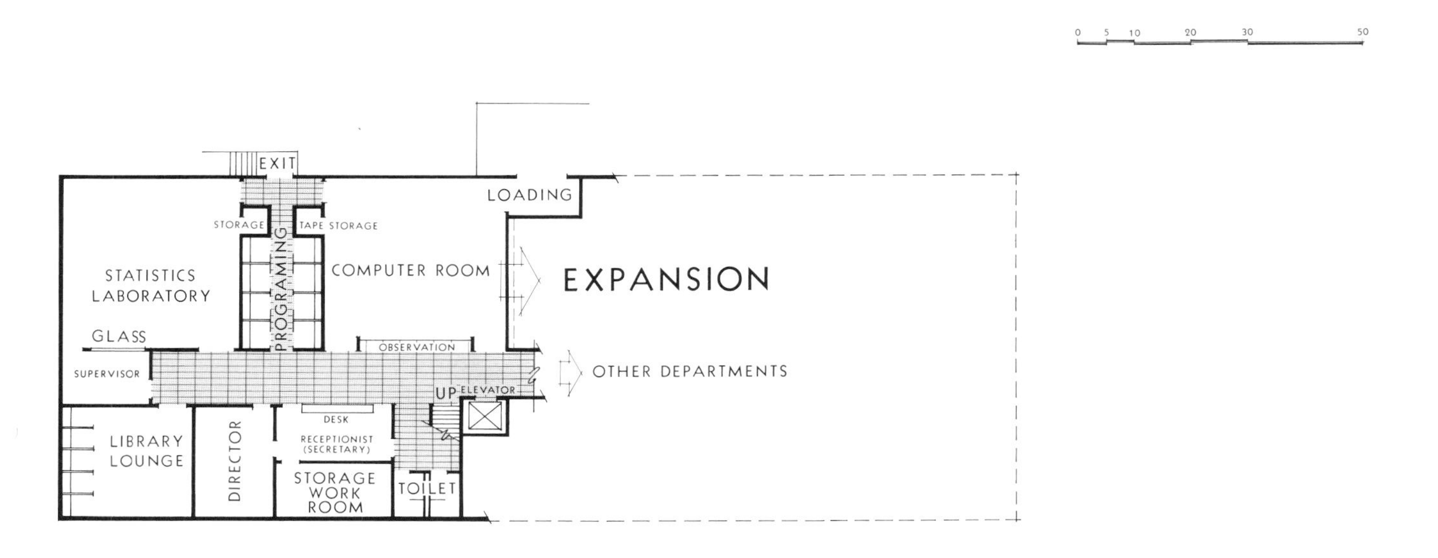

FIGURE 7 B *Small computation center and statistics laboratory in the basement of a science-mathematics building*

		Area in square feet	
		Total	*Math share*
A	Classroom space		
	1 classroom for 28–30 students (mathematics full-time)	800	800
	1 classroom for 45–54 students (mathematics half-time)	1,150	575
	Large lecture hall for 140 students	2,300	375
	TOTAL FOR A	4,250	1,750
B	Other instructional space		
	Library, housing 7,000 volumes, shared with other science departments	1,350	450
	Student study room, convertible later to library space, if necessary	1,000	400
	Divisible colloquium room, with halves serving as conference room and lounge with kitchenette	850	850
	TOTAL FOR B	3,200	1,700
C	Office space, excluding administrative area		
	Four staff offices (130–150 square feet each)	575	575
	1 staff office	200	200
	TOTAL FOR C	775	775
D	Department administration and storage space		
	Offices for chairman and associate chairman	380	380
	Reception and secretarial office	225	225
	Department workroom, mailroom, and storage	270	270
	TOTAL FOR D	875	875
U	Usable space (Sum of A, B, C, D)	9,100	5,100
S	Service and circulation areas	3,950	1,700
T	Area of floor containing mathematics facility	13,050	6,800

In addition to the floor for mathematics, the new science and mathematics building is to contain in the basement a computation center for a small electronic digital computer, together with a statistical laboratory equipped with desk calculators, an administrative headquarters for the computer, and supporting office, storage, and preparation areas. The areas of the statistical laboratory (985), the supervisor's office (160), and an estimated one third additional (380) for service and circulation should be added to the figures above to obtain the spaces assigned to mathematics and statistics: usable, 6,245; service, etc., 2,080; total, 8,325.

Basement spaces shown in Figure 7b are as follows:

		Mathematics share
E	Computation center in basement	
	Main machine room	945
	Statistical laboratory	985
	Offices for director (280), reception and secretary (200)	480
	Office for assistant (supervising statistical laboratory)	160
	Storage and workroom (200), and preparation areas (200)	400
	Library-lounge-reading room	460
	TOTAL FOR E	3,430
S	Service and circulation areas	1,140
T	Area of computation center	4,570

Plans embodying these specifications are shown in Figures 7a, b. It should be emphasized that these plans are only one suggested solution possible on a certain type of site. Site requirements cannot be overlooked in an actual building. Although these plans are not intended to be used without modification, they include certain features, helpful in planning a building, that may merit special mention.

These features are included in the mathematics floor plan (Fig. 7a):

1. The receptionist has direct access to all the offices and the workroom in the administrative complex.
2. Faculty mail slots in the mailroom are accessible in the corridor.
3. The chairman has a private exit.
4. The lounge-seminar room is a multipurpose room with a folding partition to make it available for two small group meetings at once. The room is equipped with ample chalkboard and has a small kitchenette unit and storage for extra chairs.

5 The offices of the staff are located off the main corridor in a relatively quiet area.
6 Classrooms and the large lecture hall are next to stairways for direct circulation and access.
7 A student study room provides future expansion space for the library.

These features are included in the computation center plan (Fig. 7b):

1 Viewing area for the computer room is provided opposite the main stairway where visitors may see the computer without interfering with operations.
2 An outside entrance is provided for bringing the machinery into the computer room and for bringing in supplies.
3 The statistical laboratory is convenient to the computer preparation areas and can serve as a briefing room or classroom for computer work. It can be supervised by an assistant located in an adjacent office separated by a glass partition.
4 The department secretary has access to the workroom and to the director's office, and can observe people entering the preparation areas, the statistical laboratory, and the computer library.

FACILITY FOR A UNIVERSITY OF INTERMEDIATE SIZE

Consider next a mathematics department with a present enrollment of 1,200 in a university of 5,500 students. This department expects a mathematics and statistics enrollment of 2,700 totaling 10,000 student credit hours at a saturation date ten years hence, when the university will have 10,000 students. Assume that mathematics classes are distributed as shown in the table below among the different course levels and class sizes (R denotes a recitation section meeting once a week).

The six large lecture sections could be scheduled in one large lecture hall. Fourteen classes of 33 to 42 students and six classes of 43 to 63 students could be scheduled in three classrooms seating 42, 42, and 63, respectively (Fig. 8a). The remaining 38 standard-sized classes could be scheduled in four classrooms seating 35 students and two seating 28 or 30. Most of the 44 recitation hours could be scheduled during free hours in the nine classrooms. (Scheduling difficulties would be reduced if the large lecture hall were designed to be partitioned into three small classrooms for recitation periods on certain days, but this would involve extra cost.) The colloquium room and statistical laboratory might be pressed into service as classrooms if it were necessary to add an extra section of a scheduled course at an hour when all regular classrooms were occupied. To allow more flexibility in scheduling, an extra classroom would be desirable.

To assess the staff needed to teach these 10,000 student credit hours, it is necessary to make some assumptions about the nonteaching duties of the faculty. The mathematics department (including

		Number of Mathematics Classes by Size Groups					
		Standard			*Medium*	*Large*	
Course level	*Total Enrollment*	*5–19*	*20–29*	*30–35*	*36–63*	*130–200*	*Total Classes*
Freshman	1,400	0	15 + 30R	5	5	4	29 + 30R
Sophomore	500	0	2 + 14R	2	2	2	8 + 14R
Junior and Senior	600	2	5	3	7		17
Graduate	200	5	4	1			10
	2,700	7	26 + 44R	11	14	6	64 + 44R
Number of rooms required		1	4 +	2	2	1	

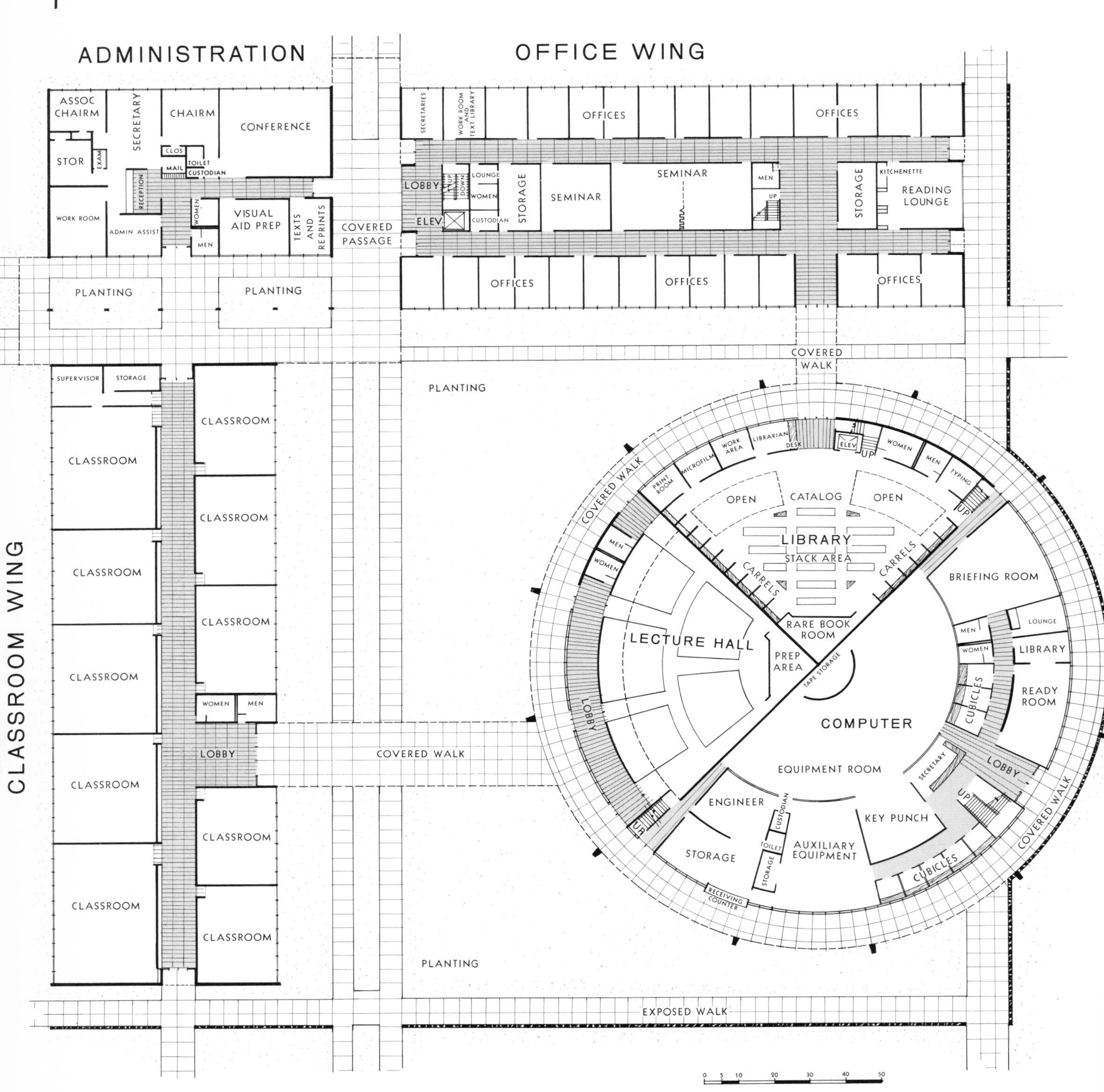

FIGURE 8 A *First floor of a building for the mathematical sciences in a university of intermediate size*

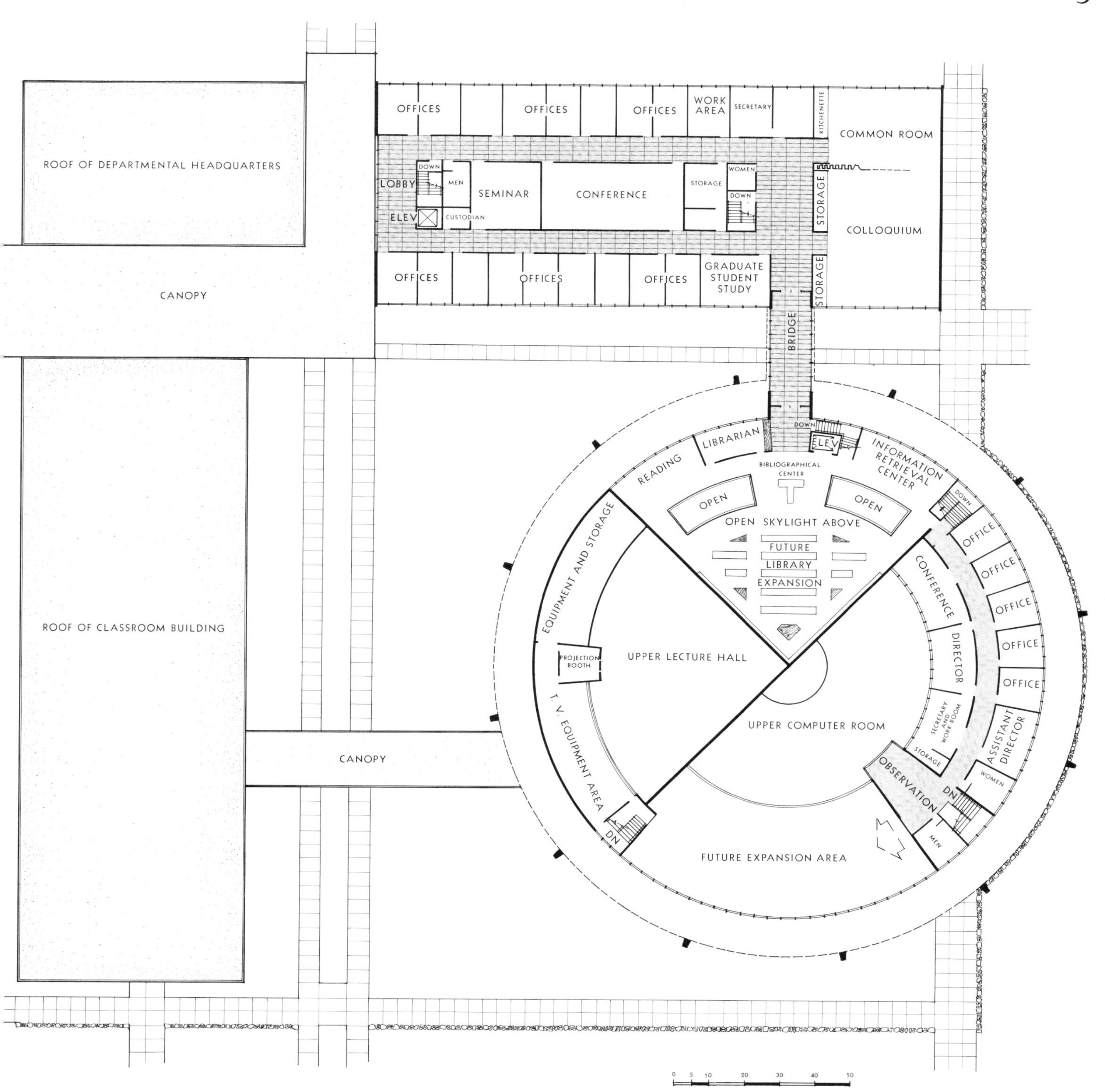

FIGURE 8 B *Second floor of a building for the mathematical sciences in a university of intermediate size*

Tarshman project, I believe.

statistics) is engaged in a graduate program for 200 graduate students, of which one-quarter to one-half are beyond the master's degree level. Guidance of M.S. and Ph.D. theses is a time-consuming occupation that does not show in the usual calculation of teaching loads. Teachers who guide research must be research workers themselves and must spend many hours a week in study not necessarily related to their classwork. Faculty members may also direct noncredit, weekly graduate seminars, not counted in their class load. Hence, typical teaching loads in a research-oriented university are lower in terms of official class hours taught than loads in a junior college or high school.

The six faculty members who teach large lecture sections might each meet one recitation section and teach one additional standard-sized class at the upper level; each would have several assistants to teach the remaining recitation sections and help with the paperwork. The chairman and associate chairman would each teach one standard-sized class. Ten other faculty members might each teach one standard-sized class and one medium-sized class (or two classes between 36 and 39) and work privately with three to six advanced graduate students. The 30 remaining classes would be taught by four additional regular faculty members or instructors (three each) and 18 teaching assistants (also teaching one recitation each). The 20 remaining recitation sections would be divided among 10 assistants. Four faculty members and 12 assistants might be assigned to research, or the research assignments might be spread part-time over a larger number of people. Two additional persons might be needed, one as supervisor of the statistical laboratory and one as an academic assistant to the chairman.

The office area should accommodate 24 regular staff members in private offices and 40 graduate assistants in offices for two, and should provide two secretarial offices with adjacent work areas, each for two secretaries or typists. An additional study room for advanced graduate students not having departmental appointments, four seminar rooms for small group meetings (including two that could be combined by opening a flexible partition), a conference room, and some storage space would also be desirable in this area. Here also would be a good place for a common room with kitchenette and a colloquium room separated from it by a flexible partition to provide expansion for a large audience.

The headquarters area should provide space for a chairman and associate chairman, and preferably for a third academic assistant, who will be needed if the administrative load is heavy. A reception area with space for three secretaries and typists should be adjacent to a workroom for duplicating equipment and a storage area for departmental supplies. An adjacent mail room should have at least 70 mail boxes opening onto the corridor. If possible the chairman's office should be next to a conference room. It would be desirable to provide space for a visual aids preparation room and for a textbook and reprint library for the department. Next to the statistical laboratory there should be office space for a supervisor of the laboratory and room for storage.

A possible architectural solution meeting these requirements for an intermediate sized facility is shown in Figures 8a, b. Space allocations (including walls) for the various components in this solution are shown on the facing page.

The following features of the facility in Figures 8a, b for a department of intermediate size may be noted:

1 Relationships between the following six components are convenient: Lecture hall to classroom area to administrative headquarters to offices to library to computation center.
2 Relationships of administrative offices to reception, secretaries, and workroom are convenient. Mail boxes are accessible from the corridor.

3 One of the classrooms for 35 students measures 28′ × 30′, although a classroom of 26′ × 30′ would seem adequate for five rows of seven seats (Fig. 22). This was because a four-foot module was adopted for the outer wall structure of this building, and it would be cheaper to give the classroom an extra two feet than to disturb the modular pattern for heating, ventilating, and fenestration.

4 The library area of 7,000 square feet should house a library of about 35,000 volumes. Most mathematics departments of the assumed size, not having more than half that many volumes, might be content with a one-story library structure for the present, using the second floor later for expansion.

5 Space for expansion on the second floor of the computation center provides for additional office area in the future.

	Area in square feet
Classroom space	
2 classrooms for 28–30 students (23′ × 28′)	1,288
4 classrooms for 35 students (3, 23′ × 32′; 1, 30′ × 28′)	3,048
2 classrooms for 42 students maximum (30′ × 32′)	1,920
1 classroom for 63 students maximum (30′ × 40′)	1,200
Large lecture hall for 200 students with space on upper level for projection booth and possible TV control booth	4,106
TOTAL FOR A	11,562

	Area in square feet
Other instructional space	
Department library, including librarian's office, information retrieval center, and study carrels	7,000
Statistical laboratory seating 36 at tables	1,080
4 seminar rooms for 15 to 20 students each	1,600
1 conference room for 30 to 40 students, outside administrative area	800
Colloquium room (40′ × 36′) including storage closets for chairs, separated by flexible partition from common room	1,440
Common room with kitchenette (24′ × 36′)	864
Reading lounge	480
TOTAL FOR B	13,264

	Area in square feet
Office space, excluding administrative area	
22 offices: 2 for secretaries, 2 serving as workrooms, 18 for staff or graduate assistants (12′ × 16′)	4,224
26 offices for staff or graduate assistants (10′ × 16′)	4,160
1 graduate student office (20′ × 16′)	320
Office for statistical laboratory supervisor	180
TOTAL FOR C	8,884

		Area in square feet
D	Department administration and storage space	
	Offices for chairman (296) and associate chairman (192)	488
	Office for administrative assistant or assistant chairman	192
	Headquarters space for reception and secretaries (3 persons)	576
	Department workroom (320), mail room (56), examination booth (24)	400
	Preparation room for visual aids	320
	Textbook and reprint library	192
	Conference room in department headquarters	832
	Storage in headquarters, including closets	270
	Storage in office and classroom areas	1,020
	TOTAL FOR D	4,290
U	Usable space, including statistics (Sum of A, B, C, D)	38,000
S	Service and circulation areas: custodian, toilets, elevators (2,200); corridors and stairways, including lockers in classroom corridor, but not including open covered area outside circular building (7,800)	10,000
T	Area servicing mathematics and statistics, excluding computation center	48,000
E	Computation Center	
	Main machine room, including tape storage	2,500
	Maintenance engineers (400), storage (500)	900
	Auxiliary equipment (750), key punch machines (400)	1,150
	Ready room (500) and 8 preparation cubicles (400)	900
	Program library, lounge and kitchenette	400
	Receptionist-dispatcher (150); secretary, workroom, and storage (250)	400
	Staff offices (2, 250 each; 5, 150 each)	1,250
	Briefing room (800), conference room (300)	1,100
	TOTAL FOR E	8,600
S	Service and circulation areas: services (500); corridors, stairways, lobby, and observation (1,900)	2,400
T	Area of computation center, not including mechanical equipment in basement $(2600 + 900)\pi$	11,000

6 Space for heating and air conditioning these buildings has not been described in the plans shown in Figures 8a, b. This might be provided in a basement area, possibly under the computer.

FACILITY FOR A LARGE UNIVERSITY As a third example, we analyze the space requirements for a combined mathematics and statistics department with a present enrollment of 4,200 in a university of 18,000 students. This department expects to serve 9,000 mathematics enrollments when the university expands to 35,000 students at the saturation date ten years hence. Assume that classes average four hours per week, so that the total number of student class hours per week will be 36,000.

An average teaching load of 300 student hours per week (e.g., 30 students 10 hours per week, or 25 students 12 hours per week) may be typical at some large institutions now, although there is wide variability in this figure. It has been assumed by many[62] that the student-staff ratio will rise by about 20 per cent in the next decade. Hence, for the purposes of this example, but without arguing the validity of this assumption, we assume that each full-time teacher will teach an average of 360 student credit hours at the saturation date. A staff teaching 100 full-time loads will be required. Some loads may be carried by two teaching fellows or graduate assistants who will share an office; others by a single staff member with a private office. In either case 100 offices are needed for the teaching staff. Additional office spaces are needed for the department administration, for the librarian, for the statistics laboratory supervisor, for 8 additional secretaries, and for 15 staff members and 30 assistants on research appointments.

In assigning classroom space, let us assume that about one-sixth of the student hours of teaching will be assigned to three large lecture rooms seating 120, 120, and 250, respectively; that nearly one-fourth of the student hours will be assigned to seven classrooms seating from 50 to 70 students, of which four will be divisible classrooms that could each accommodate two standard-sized classes of 25 to 35 students; and that the remaining hours will be assigned to two classrooms seating 35 students, 30 regular classrooms seating 28 or 30 students, and two classrooms for 25 or less. Since the two small classrooms will probably be used

Classroom space for large mathematics facility

Number of classrooms	*Type of room*	*Size of class*		*Occupancy (Hours per week)*	*Student hours*	*Total area*	*Area per student hour*
		Maximum	*Average*				
1 L*	Trapezoid	250	150	20 × 1	3,000	3,400	1.13
2 L	Trapezoid	120	80	20 × 2	3,200	3,600	1.12
1 D†	35′ × 40′	70	47	30 × 1	1,410	1,400	.99
2 D	30′ × 40′	60	40	30 × 2	2,400	2,400	1.00
2	30′ × 36′	54	36	30 × 2	2,160	2,160	1.00
2 (1D)	27′ × 40′	50	35	30 × 2	2,100	2,160	1.03
2	30′ × 24′	36(35)	28	30 × 2	1,680	1,440	.86
30	30′ × 20′	30(28)	21.5	30 × 30	19,350	18,000	.93
2	27′ × 20′	25(24)	14	25 × 2	700	1,080	1.53
37 + 3L + 4D				1,280	36,000	35,640	.99

* L = Lecture room
† D = Divisible room

	Area in square feet
Classroom space	
3 large lecture rooms	7,000
7 medium-sized classrooms (4 divisible)	8,120
34 standard-sized classrooms	20,520
TOTAL FOR A	35,640
Other instructional space	
Library, including 4 small discussion rooms	8,100
3 student study areas (each about 800)	2,400
9 conference rooms (1,200; 800; 7, each 400)	4,800
10 seminar rooms (7, each 400; 3, each 256)	3,568
Top-floor colloqium room	1,344
Top-floor lounge area with kitchenette	1,260
2 statistical laboratories (2,112; 1,296) with desk calculators	3,408
TOTAL FOR B	24,880
Office space (excluding administrative area)	
73 offices for 70 faculty and 6 assistants (15′ × 10′)	10,950
60 "double" offices for 114 assistants and 6 secretaries (15′ × 12.5′)	11,250
2 large offices for librarian and 2 secretaries	600
TOTAL FOR C	22,800

		Area in square feet
D	Department administration and storage space	
	3 offices (chairman, 400; associate chairman, 208; assistant chairman, 208)	816
	Reception area and secretarial pool (3 persons)	832
	Mail room (192), duplicating room with safe (640)	832
	Texts and reprints (208), visual aid preparation (312)	520
	Conference room (480), adjoining office or seminar room (480)	960
	Headquarters space for waiting, circulation, and closets	400
	Department storage areas (800 + 240 + 11 × 60 + 100)	1,800
	TOTAL FOR D	6,160
U	Usable space (sum of A, B, C, D)	89,480
S	Service and circulation areas (23.3% of total)	27,240
T	Area of building (excluding heating and air conditioning)	116,720

for a number of classes of five to ten students, the efficiency of use is likely to be low. Furthermore, the large lecture sections may fill very well at popular hours of the day, but may be less than half full at hours considered undesirable by students.

The 41 classrooms and 3 lecture rooms to accommodate 1,280 class hours of teaching with 36,000 student hours might be distributed in size and use as in the table on page 28. The "occupancy" column gives the number of hours per week that each classroom is expected to be used, times the number of classrooms of that size. The "student hours" figure is obtained by multiplying the average class size for the room by the expected number of hours per week of occupancy for the room. In most cases the classroom area per student hour of use comes out close to one square foot. The total area provided is approximately 35,640 square feet, including walls.

The choice between the two values for the maximum number of student stations in the smaller classrooms depends on whether the front board is on a short or a long side of the rectangle. The latter arrangement is preferable for the teacher and class but allows slightly fewer seats. Space assignments for the large facility shown in Figures 10a, b, c, d are listed above.

The architectural solution in Figures 9 and 10a, b, c, d for the large facility for mathematics and statistics includes the following features:

1 Classroom areas with heavy traffic are on the first two floors, and the third floor library is between the student area and faculty office area above.
2 Four divisible classrooms permit double use by small classes. Two of these share a rear screen-projection room with the adjacent corner rooms on the second floor. This floor, on which the

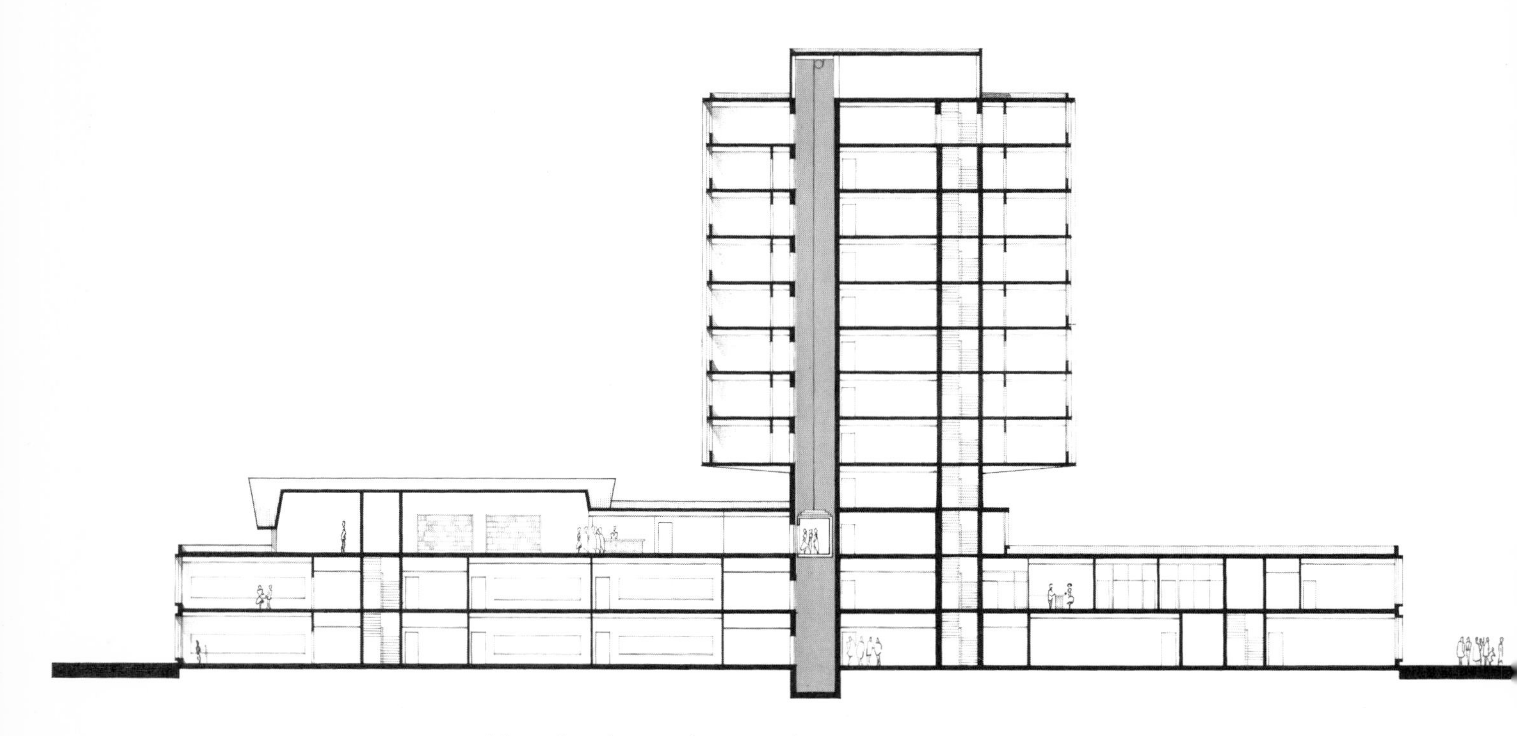

FIGURE 9 A *Building for the mathematical sciences in a large university. Front view showing classrooms on first and second floors, administrative headquarters second floor right, library third floor left, and offices in tower*

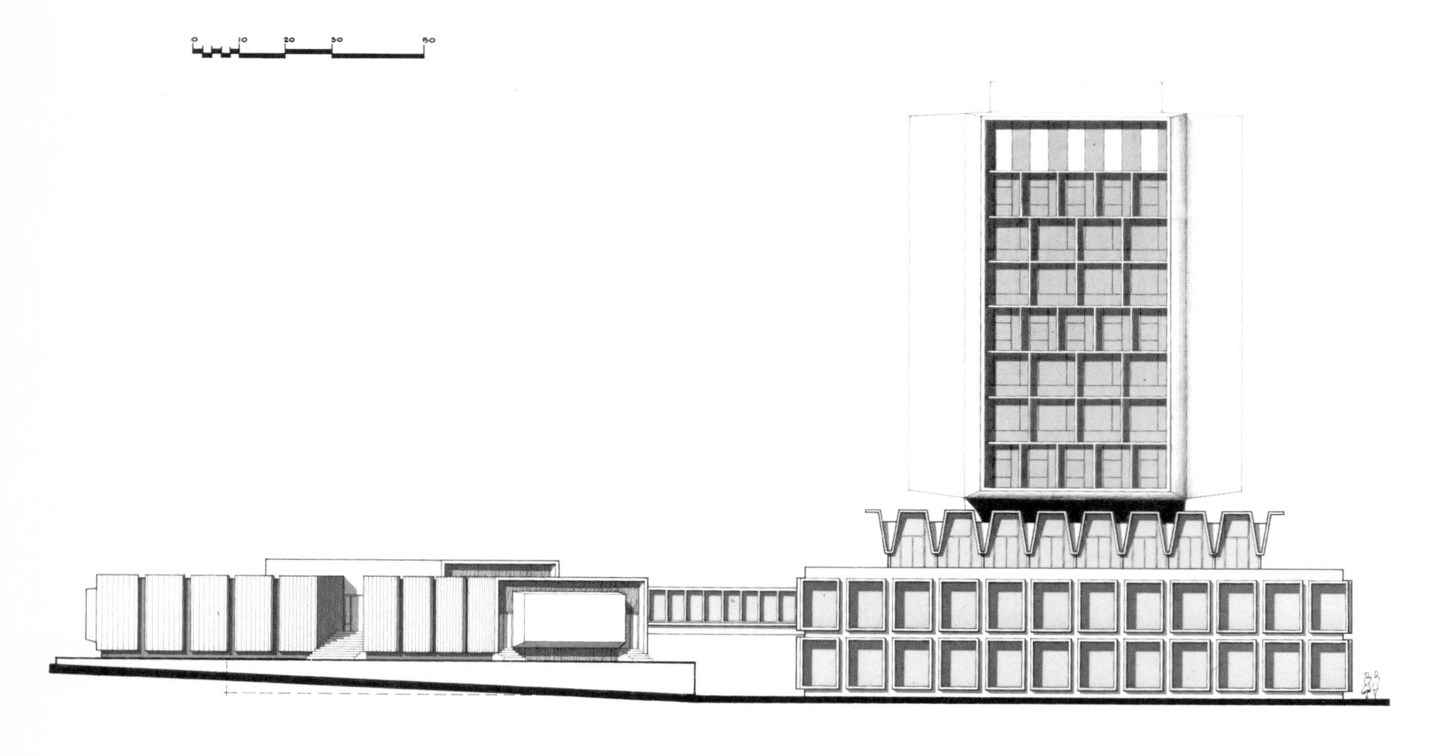

FIGURE 9 B *Building for the mathematical sciences in a large university. Side view showing adjacent triangular auditorium building at left*

visual aids preparation room is located, is also connected to the common lobby of the three auditoriums.

3 The auditoriums, fitted together in a triangular building, may be entered from the ground floor at the vertices of the triangle, or from the second floor lobby connected by a bridge to the department headquarters and second floor classrooms. The aisles are steeply sloped for better visibility.

4 The departmental headquarters includes almost all the features recommended in Chapter 7. Note that the mailroom has ample wall space for 200 mail boxes (10 rows of 10 boxes on each of its two corridor walls, if boxes are 1 foot wide and 6 inches high in outside dimensions), and that it is close to the receptionist for telephone messages and to the duplicating room for announcements and examinations. A design like the 10 × 10 orthogonal Latin square decoration in the new mathematics building at Dartmouth College might appropriately decorate the mailboxes.

5 The chairman has a private washroom, and his office is next to the conference room and to his secretary. He can depart through the back corridor and stairway without having to go by the reception desk.

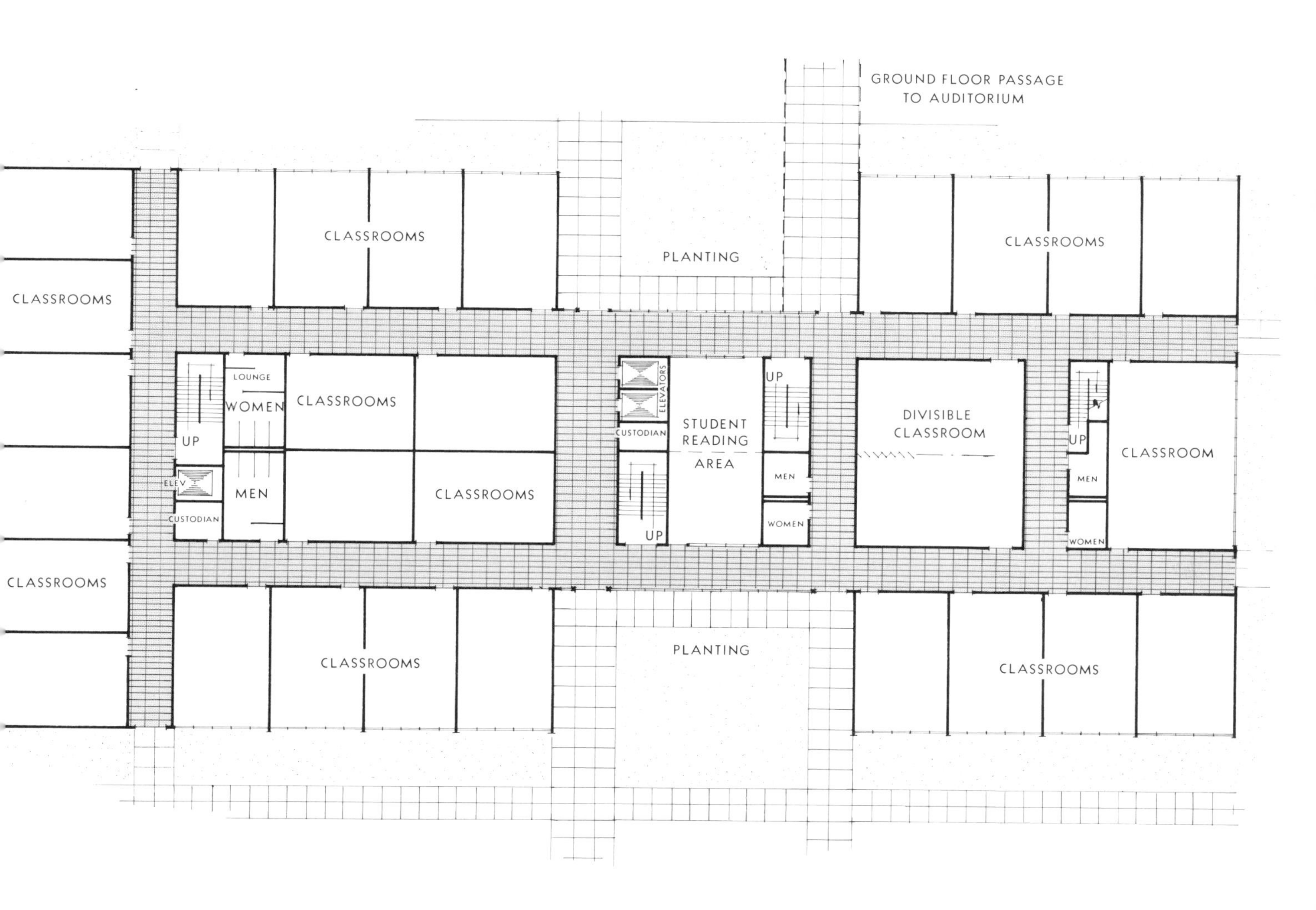

FIGURE 10 A *Ground floor of the building in Figure 9* A, B *showing 28 classrooms*

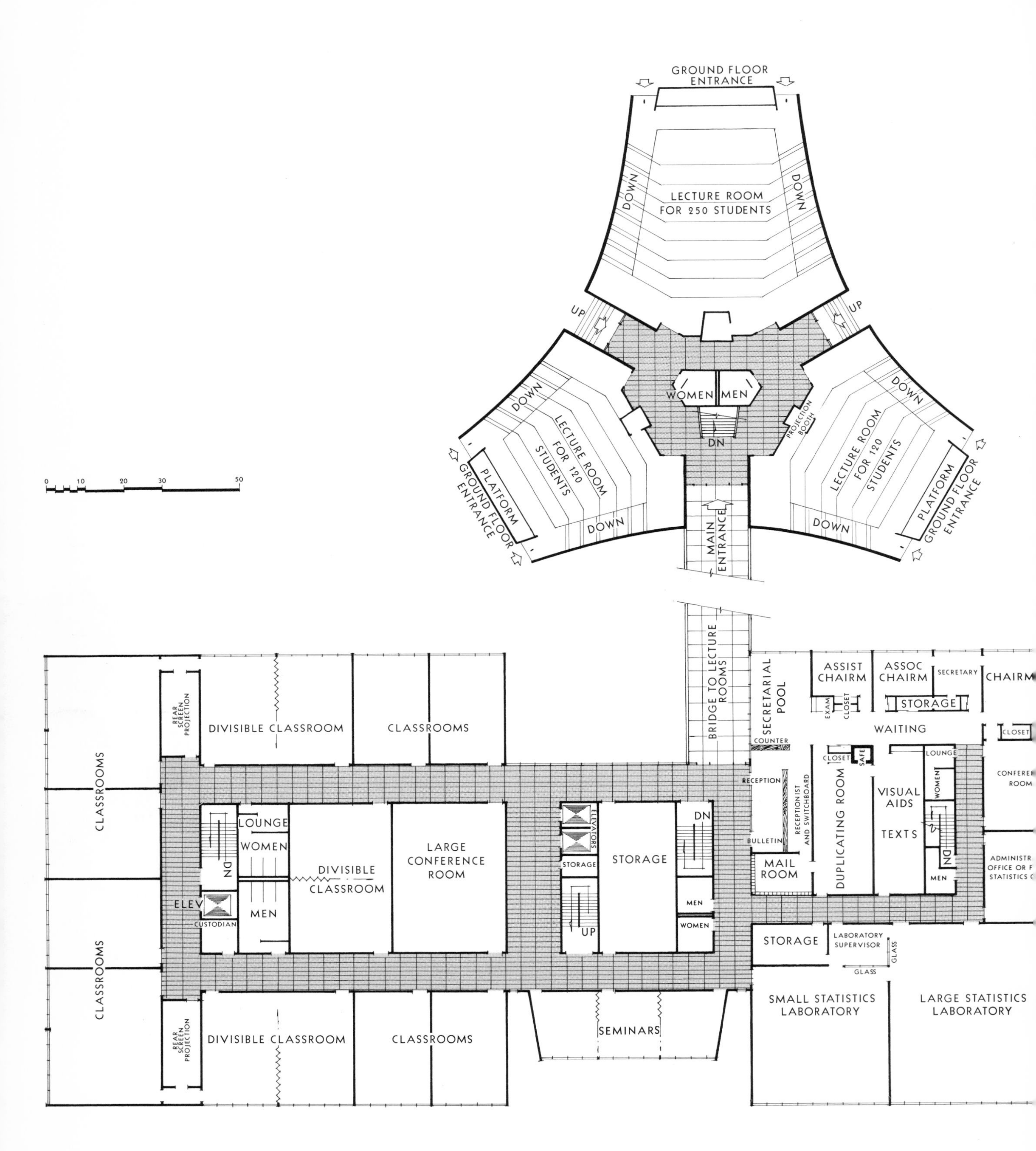

FIGURE 10 B *Second floor of the building in Figures 9 A, B*

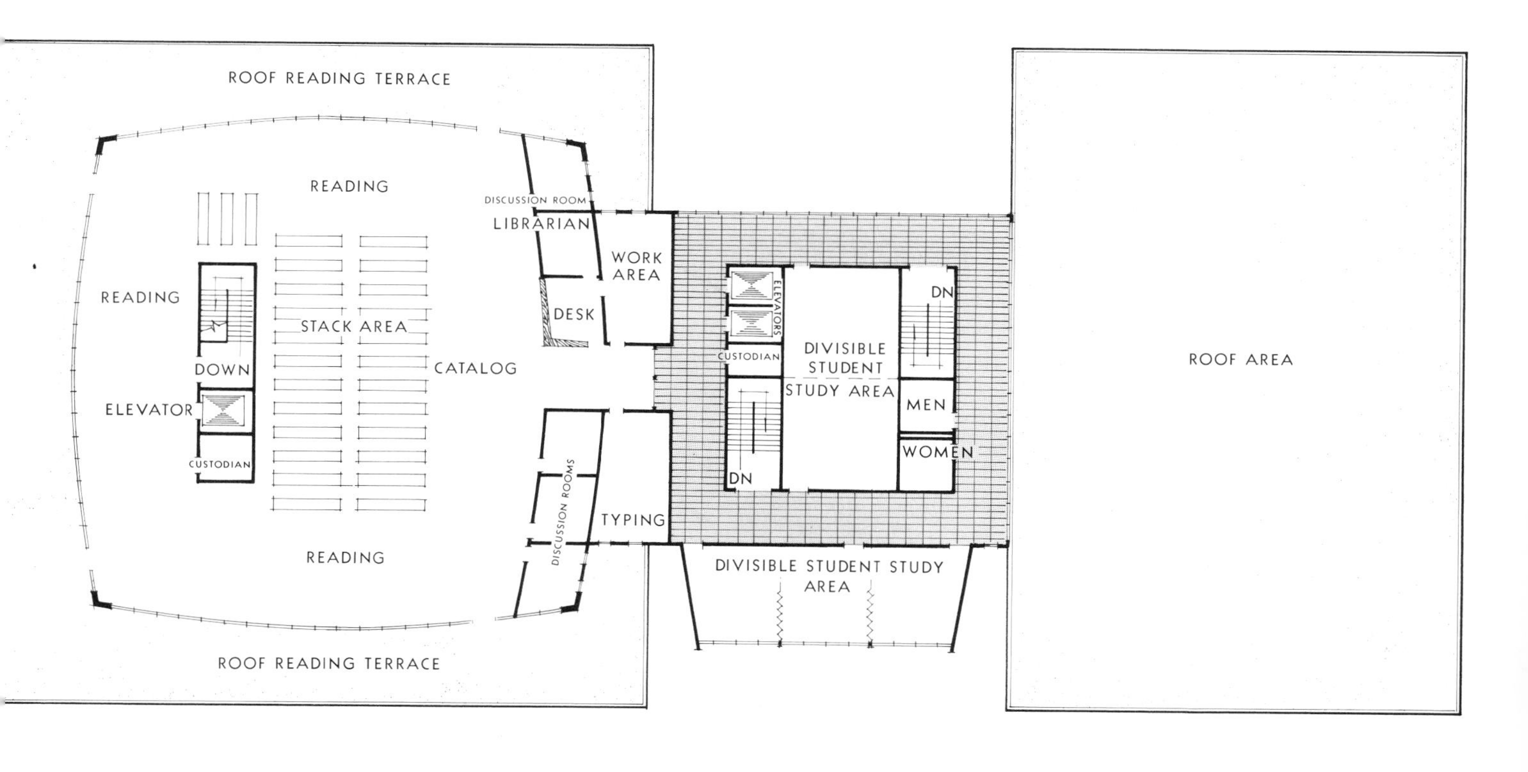

FIGURE 10 C *Third floor (showing library) of the building in Figures 9* A, B

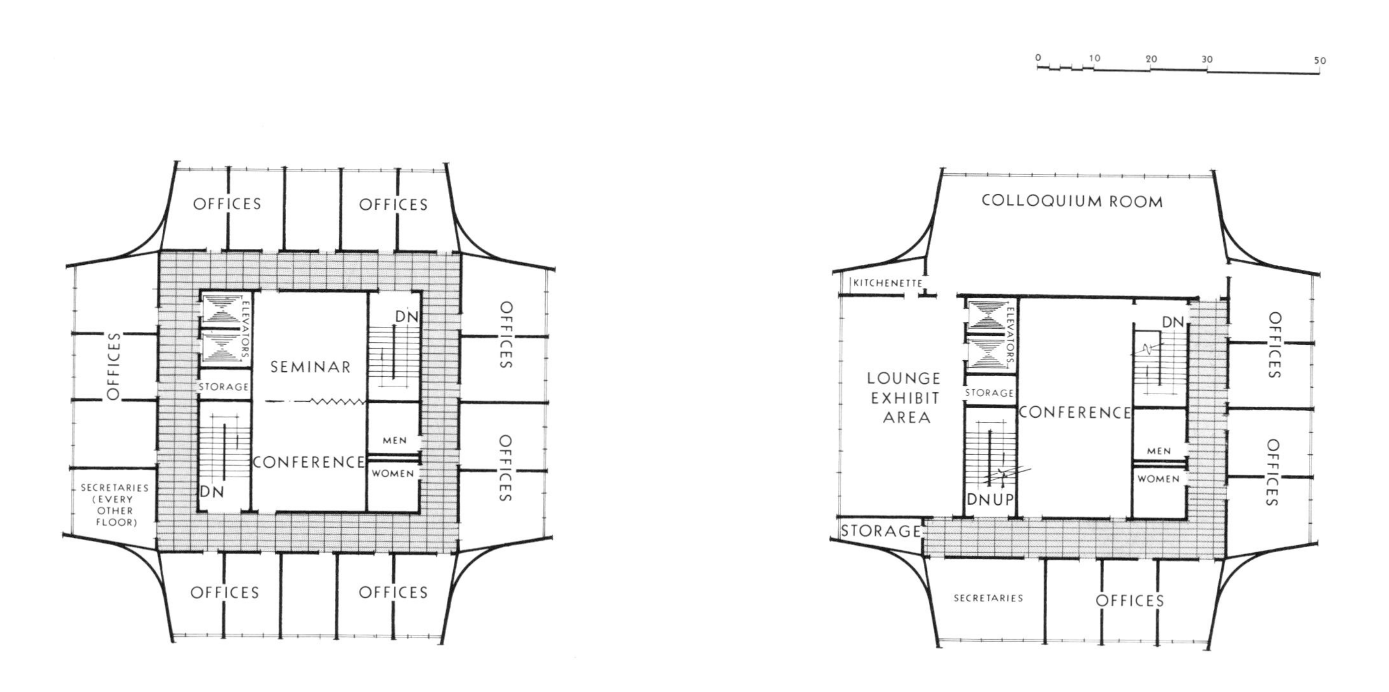

FIGURE 10 D *Upper floors and top floor of the office tower of the building in Figures 9* A, B

6 A 20′ × 24′ room between the conference room and the large statistical laboratory could accommodate a future office for a statistics chairman and his secretary, if a separate statistics department were formed at a later date. The new department could share the adjacent conference room, the mail room, duplicating room, and visual aids room, with the mathematics department.

7 If a small electronic computer were needed by the mathematics department for instructional use, it might be installed in one of the two statistical laboratories, leaving the other one for desk calculators. The room suggested above as a possible statistics headquarters would then be used by computer personnel instead.

8 A large storage room for the department is provided on the second floor in a 20′ × 40′ room by the elevator. This room would hold desks, chairs, and large visual aid equipment to be used with the lecture halls and second floor classrooms. A smaller storage room (12′ × 20′) is available near the duplicating room for departmental supplies. Convenient storage for the faculty on each floor is provided by a 10′ × 6′ closet (about 5 or 6 feet of shelf space per office), although more space than this might be worthwhile.

9 The lounge area by the colloquium room on the top floor (suggested by the new Mathematics Building at the University of Wisconsin) provides a pleasant place with an excellent view where faculty members can gather before a colloquium talk to exchange ideas (Fig. 42). Chalkboard should be mounted on one or possibly two of the wall areas.

INSTRUCTIONAL SPACE PER STUDENT CREDIT HOUR

Subtotals in the three space analyses described above may be compared as shown in the table at the head of the next column. These subtotals include the statistical laboratory and adjoining supervisor's office in the small facility, but exclude the computation centers.

Size of facility	*Small*	*Medium*	*Large*
Mathematics Enrollment			
students	400	2,700	9,000
student credit hours	1,460	10,000	36,000
Areas in square feet			
A Classroom space	1,750	11,562	35,640
B Other instructional space	2,685	13,264	24,880
C Office space (excluding administrative area)	935	8,884	22,800
D Department administration and storage space	875	4,290	6,160
U Usable space (Sum of A, B, C, D, part of E)	6,245	38,000	89,480
S Service and circulation areas	2,080	10,000	27,240
T Total area for mathematics and statistics, excluding computation center, heating, etc.	8,325	48,000	116,720
Areas in square feet per student credit hour			
A Classroom space per student credit hour	1.20	1.16	0.99
U Usable space per student credit hour	4.28	3.80	2.49
T Total space per student credit hour	5.70	4.80	3.24

It is interesting to compare the three architectural solutions on the basis of space per student credit hour of instruction. On this basis the large facility is seen to be the most efficient in space utilization.

Instructional space per full-time student in the institutions of higher education in the United States in 1960 was about 125 square feet; this same figure has been used by the U.S. Office of Education in estimating space needs for the period 1960–1970.[62] Assuming that the average load of a full-time student is about 15 or 16 hours, we obtain a quotient of instructional space per student credit hour amounting to 8 square feet gross, or 6 square feet "usable" (including mechanical equipment). It would seem that laboratory sciences and the fine arts require more than the average amount of space per student and that mathematics and statistics may require somewhat less than the average of 6 square feet of usable space.

Recognizing that these figures are heavily influenced by the efficiency of room utilization, by the size of the library, and by the extent of nonteaching responsibilities, it may still be helpful to note that an approximate range of square feet per student credit hour may be between 1.0 and 1.2 for classroom space, between 2.4 and 4.5 for usable space for mathematics and statistics, and between 3.2 and 6.0 for gross space (excluding the computation center and the mechanical equipment for heating and air conditioning).

Cooperative planning: educational, architectural, and financial

The broad areas of responsibility in planning can be assigned to three groups of people:

A The educational group for whom the building is to be built: department chairman, department planning director, faculty, secretarial and custodial staff, students, and others.

B The professional group responsible for the technical aspects of the project: the architect and his consultants, and land and campus planners.

C The administrative group responsible for the business and financial arrangements: Board of Trustees, the president or his representative, business and financial officers.

Together these groups must balance the desirable goals set forth in the educational specifications (p. 38) against the limitations of the site and the budget. While each group will explore its own area of responsibility with many other subgroups, committees, and individual experts and consultants, there are definite points at which coordination is necessary for proper evaluation of progress and accomplishment (Fig. 11). Whether the evaluation is done by a high-level steering committee, an outside educational consultant, or even by the Board of Trustees itself, the weighing of need against cost is a vitally necessary and continuing function in the preparation of an educational program.

RELATIONSHIP TO OTHER DEPARTMENTS In choosing a site for a new building it is important for a college or university to have a master plan for the growth and development of its campus that will produce a well-coordinated pattern of buildings instead of a collection of unrelated units. In the development of a campus site (see Fig. 5), thought should be given to patterns of traffic between various parts of the institution so as to centralize certain facilities (for example, the library and possibly the computation center) and minimize the distance that students must travel between classes. Even where land may be available for horizontal growth, it may be better for a building to go up[68] rather than out in order that students may be able to go from one class to the next in the allotted time regardless of the weather.

Since mathematics is required of students in engineering and physical sciences, and frequently in social sciences and other disciplines, the mathematics department should if possible have a central location. Every major department of mathematics should have either its own library or a library shared with other departments in the same building. In smaller institutions, if the mathematics department is not within a five-minute walk of the central library, there should be a separate library for mathematics books in the mathematics building, possibly shared with other departments. If the mathematics department is to share a library with statistics and the computing center, these departments should be near each other. Also, if large lecture rooms are to be shared by several departments, it is preferable that these rooms be easily accessible to the departments involved.

The role of the department in planning

The planning of any new building or facility should be a cooperative effort of the administrative officers responsible for the project, the architects, and the people who are to use the building.

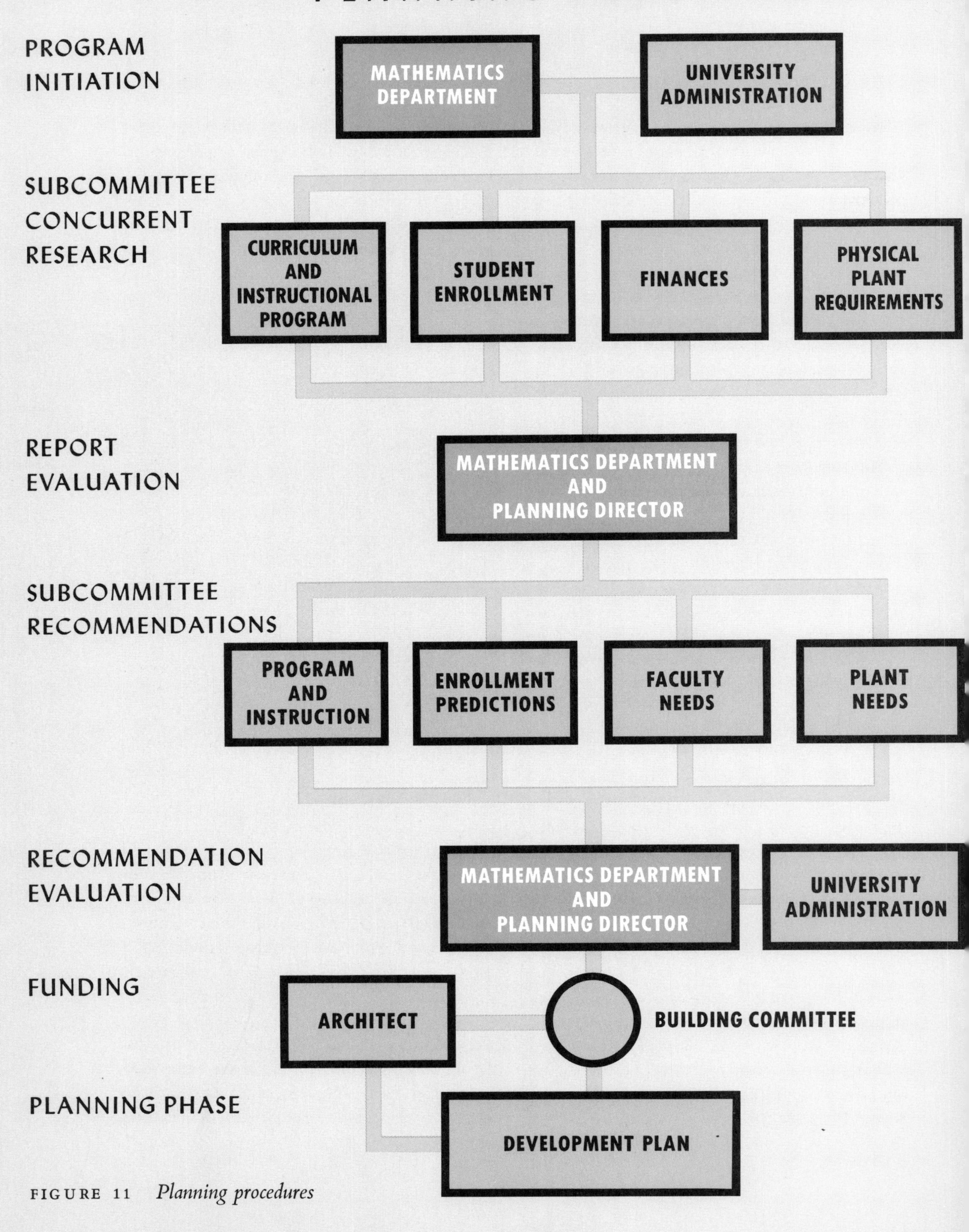

FIGURE 11 *Planning procedures*

When the building is to serve mathematics, or statistics, or computer science, people in these disciplines should be consulted in more than a perfunctory way; they should take an active part in its planning.

DEPARTMENTAL PLANNING DIRECTOR The department should select one of its members to serve as departmental planning director with released time to "live with" the building and become completely immersed in its planning. He should work with the planning architect, not merely with intermediaries. He should know the needs of the department (and not underestimate them!), and he should have enough stature to carry his weight with the administrators and architects involved and be able to say "No" when necessary. Besides the departmental planning director himself, every person with a direct interest in the final result—chairman, staff members, students, secretaries, and maintenance personnel—should be drawn into the planning.

Attention should be given at the outset both to the quantitive space needs already discussed and to the proper relationships between spaces for classrooms, lecture halls, offices, the library, the administrative headquarters, and storage areas. Future methods of instruction should be considered that may include the use of large lecture sections, audio-visual aids, or television. Facilities for research should not be overlooked. Having examined the functions of the building from the point of view of the department, the planning director should present his findings clearly in writing to the architect and the administration.

After a preliminary decision has been made regarding the location and size of offices, the future occupants might well be asked to submit to the planning director sketches showing their preferences for the arrangement of office furnishings and built-in equipment, including telephone and electrical outlets, bookshelves and chalkboards. Of course, the planning director, together with the chairman and architect, must protect the department from special requests by individual faculty members that would make any of the offices or other spaces undesirable for use by others in the future, and they must also consider how special requests may affect costs.

PROGRAMING A BUILDING The term *programing* as used in building design includes the collection of requirements for the building in the light of its functions, communication of these requirements to the architect, and supervision of the incorporation of these ideas into a building design. The steps in planning and constructing a building fall into three major phases: 1) the planning phase, in which major ideas are worked out and preliminary drawings are agreed upon; 2) the intermediate phase, including the preparation, review and acceptance of the final drawings, the selection of contractors for bids, and the award of contract; and 3) the construction phase up to the acceptance of the building.

In preliminary conferences between the architect and departmental representatives, the latter should contribute carefully prepared and documented statements on the specific functions to be served by the new building, and the architect should use his planning skill and knowledge of construction and equipment to suggest designs for a building to serve these functions.

IMAGINATIVE THINKING Planning a building requires not only a comprehensive view of the needs of today, but imaginative thinking about the needs of the next decade or two. What changes may occur in the pattern of mathematics instruction in the next decade? Will programed learning or teaching machines contribute to increase the effectiveness of individual study? Will the computer be employed part time to operate teaching machines or to assist in searching the literature? What new methods of information retrieval will be developed, and what types of space will they require? Will the library be copying brief articles from reference books or journals quickly for the use of students and staff, rather than permitting these books or journals to be taken out? Will library information more commonly be stored on microfilm or magnetic tape? What provision should be made for the use and storage of overhead projectors and the preparation of overlays? Should conduits be provided through which television cables can be strung, rather than building in cables which may rapidly obsolesce? Will some elementary mathematics classes be taught in appropriate classrooms built in dormitories to minimize student traffic? Will the year-round use of facilities require air-conditioning? Has adequate provision been made for expansion? Is there sufficient flexibility in certain parts of a building to permit reassignment of spaces to other uses?

A good building will remain standing long after its planners have retired. Whenever the budget permits, the building should be planned to serve not only the needs of today or of the year of completion, but also the anticipated needs for the foreseeable future. Unfortunately, budget limitations have often caused a new facility to be inadequate from the start. On the other hand, if a building is built to serve a growing department adequately for ten years, thought must be given to the manner of sharing the space before projected growth justifies its exclusive use. If another department is to share the space temporarily at the beginning, will it have space of its own to move into in a few years, so that the temporary sharing arrangement does not become permanent?

EDUCATIONAL SPECIFICATIONS AND OBJECTIVES The educational programing, when completed, generally results in a written document sometimes referred to as "educational specifications." While these specifications will serve primarily as guidelines for the architect in the preparation of his planning and design studies, they also serve as a "public relations" vehicle by outlining the needs and aims of the educational program or curriculum to be housed in the proposed facility.

The educational specifications must include more than a bare statistical listing of the spaces and square feet needed. Such a minimal approach is totally unrealistic, and it is insufficient for the guidance of the architect. Indeed, the educational specifications should explain to the architect in some detail the educational philosophy and objectives of the department. They should explain the methodology and techniques to be used in teaching and curriculum development, and the relationships that should exist between instructional areas, offices, and the library, and between faculty offices and administration. Attention must be drawn in the educational specifications to enrollment projections and teacher supply. These and a host of other vital problems must be discussed in terms of demonstrable educational needs, both for the architect's edification and to crystallize the staff's current and long-range thinking.

EDUCATIONAL PROGRAMING A clear-cut statement of the objectives to be attained is essential if a completed building is to serve satisfactorily the purposes for which it is designed. Programing the requirements for a building can be time-consuming and often frustrating to those unaccustomed to making judgments and decisions in such a project. Those who believe that blueprints can be drawn and construction started before adequate detailed planning, have a shortsighted approach that inevitably leads to complaints. If the preliminary educational programing of needs and requirements is lacking or incomplete, the architect must fill the void by either calling on his own previous experience or assembling a program by bits and pieces. Cooperation is needed to avoid the obvious pitfalls of such negative planning.

SPACE ADEQUACY DETERMINATIONS Those responsible for establishing space needs for a proposed building need to know that the requirements stated in the educational specifications will provide a facility that is neither too small nor too large. The major factors determining costs are the area and volume of the structure, although costs may also be affected by market conditions and the time of bidding. The efficient use of space saves money, and the provision of spaces rarely used results in higher average costs per space-time unit. Standards have been developed for measuring space adequacy and efficiency of utilization, based on the rate of occupancy of student stations, both for secondary and higher education. A standard survey form has been prepared by the California State Department of Education that will help to determine the adequacy and efficiency of a proposed project design. Also, the Educational Facilities Laboratories, Inc., has recently published a report on the utilization and planning of instructional facilities in small colleges, entitled "To Build or Not to Build."[66]

BUDGET ESTIMATING AND BALANCING An average unit cost figure is applied to the gross total area (p. 20) to approximate construction costs for the structure itself. In some cases this unit cost may be estimated by the institution or by the school system on the basis of past or present experience with similar buildings.[13,28] A facilities survey showed that construction costs for instructional buildings had increased about 43 per cent in the 1950's and averaged about $20 per square foot in 1959 for the actual building construction, not including the auxiliary costs discussed below.[62] Cost figures vary with the type of construction, with the locality, and with time. The experienced architect can be helpful in arriving at current approximate costs in the given locality for budgeting purposes. He can also note any peculiar considerations in the project or unusual conditions in the terrain which would seriously affect the application of the customary unit cost figure.

In addition to the cost of the structure itself, the project appropriation figure includes auxiliary costs, which amounted to an additional 50 per cent of building costs in the facilities survey cited above. These are the costs of the land, roads, walks, driveways, parking areas, covered passageways, landscaping, utility and service connections, street lighting, equipment, furniture and furnishings, and other items that should not be overlooked. It may be possible for the architect on the basis of experience to assign a lump sum to such items. Furthermore, it is well to include in the budget an item of possibly 3 to 5 per cent of the total construction cost for unforeseen contingencies.

If estimated costs exceed the available funds, some difficult decision making becomes necessary. Any building project reaches fruition only as a result of a series of compromises or value judgments. Representatives of the educational, architectural, and administrative groups involved in the planning must reach a decision on a compromise plan that will not seriously affect the adequacy of the educational program which the building is to house. At this point the departmental planning director must know what is indispensable for proper operation of the department at a date, possibly two to five years later, when the building will be completed.

The role of the architect

THE REQUIREMENTS, SITE, AND BUDGET The architect, in approaching the design phase of a project, must thoroughly familiarize himself with three basic factors: 1) the requirements, 2) the site, and 3) the budget (Fig. 12). He must not only gather all pertinent information relating to these factors before he begins his design studies, but he must also satisfy himself at the outset that there is a

FIGURE 12 *Requirements, site, budget*

feasible, practical balance between these elements. Reluctance of an architect to undertake his initial studies because of an imbalance between requirements and available funds should be taken as a warning of possible trouble to come. Too often, enthusiastic individuals or institutions, anxious to get a building under way, will cajole their architect into preparing drawings that should hopefully include some magic formula to reduce costs just for them. The most favorable circumstances cannot be assured in the planning stages. To initiate a project on the basis of wishful thinking is impractical. Before the architect proceeds with his design studies, it is important to secure general agreement among the responsible parties concerning the major aspects of the program and the budget. Substantive changes in location or requirements, made after drawings are begun, can only result in added costs and delays.

THE EFFECT OF THE SITE Whenever possible, the architect should be consulted before a firm commitment is made on a site. His evaluation of a site is made not alone on "eye-appeal," but on a study of the adaptability of the site to the type of building to be placed thereon, as well as on such mundane but vital matters as the availability of water supply, sewage disposal, storm sewers, utility connections, and a host of other site considerations often overlooked.[18]

The site upon which the proposed facility is to be built can have considerable effect on the final cost of the project, particularly if abnormal subsurface conditions are present or, even worse, are disclosed during construction. It is therefore essential that the architect be furnished as early as possible with an adequate topographic survey of the site, and with data from test borings and soil analyses.

STAGES IN THE DESIGN PROCESS A fairly uniform and logical procedure, common to all architects, emerges in the step-by-step progression from the initial study of a building design to the completion of construction. The four stages in this pattern are as follows: A. schematic design studies; B. preliminary design development; C. final working drawings and specifications; and D. construction.

A. SCHEMATIC DESIGN STUDIES Once he has all the basic information before him, the architect commences a series of graphic analyses, more in the nature of graphic research than of definitive planning. These are highly important to the success of the finished building, for it is at this earliest conceptual stage that major design decisions are made. The architect analyzes and evaluates mentally and on paper the various pertinent aspects of the total problem, and he determines the relative weight to be assigned to each element. First, he must consider the various uses of the building, their relationship to each other in terms of circulation patterns, and the relationship of this building to others on campus, both architecturally and

DESIGN PROGRAM

in use (Fig. 13). These relationships assume, of course, that a master-plan for ultimate campus development has already been prepared and that the architect must now accommodate his mathematics building to it. He must pay due respect to the objectives laid down by the master-plan without violating his own planning principles, and certainly without suppressing his own design judgments for the sake of a rigid, monotonous conformity. Harmony between diverse building types and styles can be achieved by a sensitive architect working with a client who is understanding, not dogmatic. Although the architect is dealing with broad unit-blocks of space during the schematic stage, he must always relate these to the specific site. The terrain itself can be a deciding factor, for example, in establishing the number of stories for the proposed building.

Factors affecting the placement of the building on the site include (Fig. 14):

1 *Access*—The existing or proposed road pattern of the campus will determine the location of entrance drives, etc., and hence may well determine the location of many elements of the building design. For example, the placement of service elements, boiler rooms, and kitchens may be influenced by the location of an existing service road. Similarly, the location of public-use areas of a building, such as auditoriums, library, and administrative offices, will be influenced by the location of the principal entrance drive, as projected on the master site plan.

2 *Physical Attributes*—The architect will wish to take advantage of whatever natural resources the site may contain—groves of trees, ponds, rivers, etc. Even the high and low ground areas may determine to some degree the shape and arrangement of the building elements.

3 *Regulatory Agencies*—There are times when local building and zoning regulations may place limiting restrictions on both the building and the site-development aspects of the architect's design.

4 *Climate and Orientation*—The general climate of the area, as well as the microclimate at the building site itself, may govern the placement of building elements; for example, a site sloping up to the north, or down to the west, may call for two entirely different solutions. Similarly, placement of the building with respect to the sun can affect the design by influencing the fenestration pattern or by requiring the use of exterior solar shielding.

5 *Sound and Noise*—The presence of noise-making sources, such as arterial highways, railroads, and airports off campus, or playing fields, maintenance shops, dining halls, and kitchens on campus, may influence building placement on a site.

6 *Parking*—No discussion of site development would be complete without adequate consideration of the problem of automobile parking.[41] One acre of parking space will accommodate at most about 120 standard-sized cars or 150 foreign cars. If the master site plan for campus development has made adequate provisions for parking, this problem does not require special consideration in planning a mathematics facility. However, the architect must be made aware of his responsibility in the matter, so that if necessary he may reserve certain neighboring areas for parking. In planning a computation center he should know whether computation services for off-campus users may require some nearby visitor- or public-parking areas.

To the uninitiated, much time appears to be spent in fixing the design—sometimes slightingly referred to as "playing with blocks"—with very

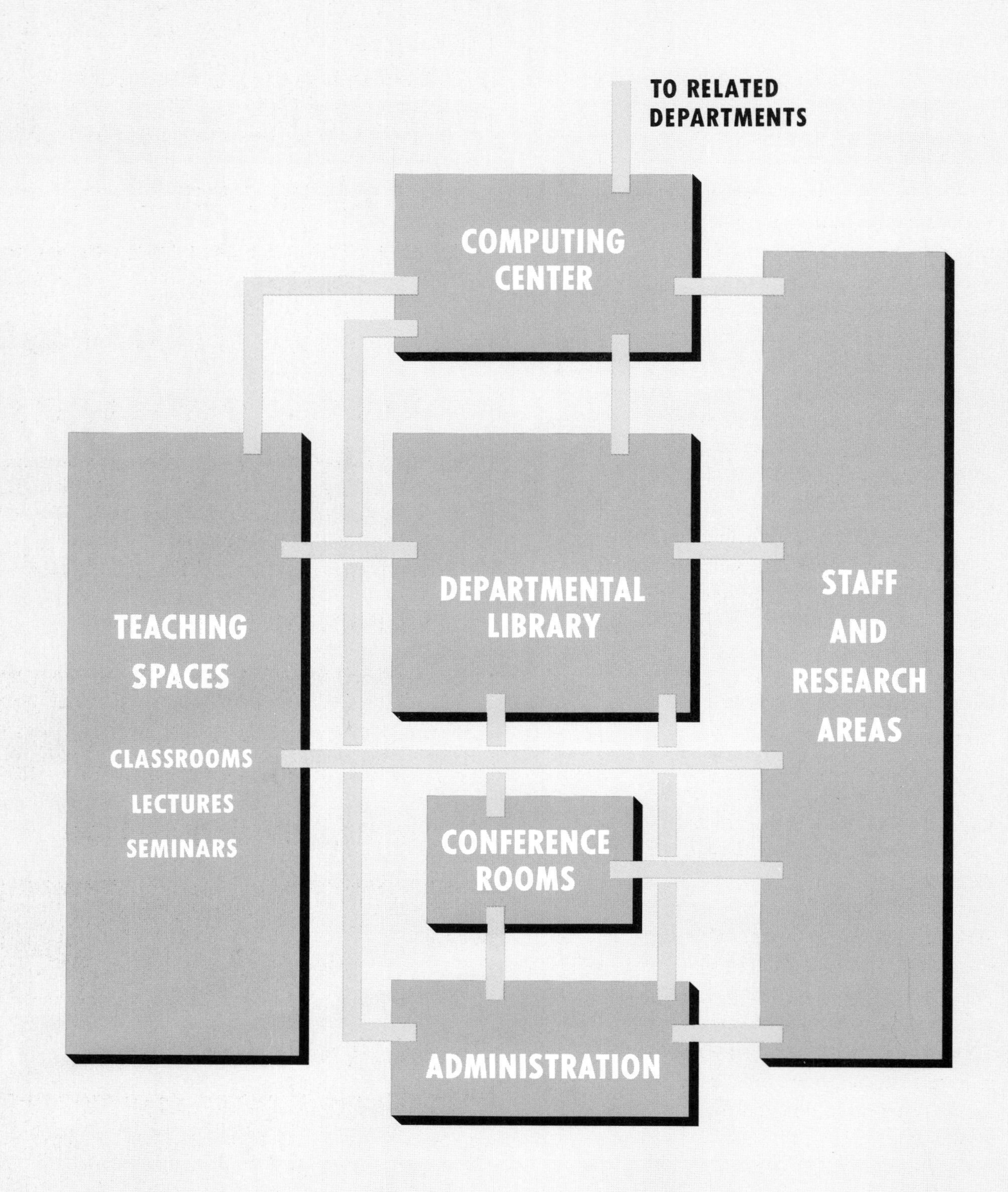

FIGURE 13 *Departmental relatedness*

little to show for the effort. Yet this stage is the heart of the design process on which depends to a large degree the ultimate success or failure of the project to serve its primary purpose. The architect tries and discards one scheme after another, revising and refining each solution as he goes, until he reaches a solution that meets all requirements and satisfies his aesthetic sense in both mass and scale. The members of the planning committee representing the mathematics department and the university administration should cooperate with the architect and actively participate in the development of the architectural solution. By suggestion and criticism, as well as by reappraisal of their own criteria, they will give direction and purpose to the undertaking. Only when general accord has been reached as to the validity of the whole planning approach will the architect be ready to proceed to the second major stage of design development. He will then have before him the broad conceptual basis for the building design, its relation to site, and its cost feasibility.

B. PRELIMINARY DESIGN DEVELOPMENT The "definitive" stage of preliminary design involves the actual planning arrangements for the building itself, or for a complex of unit buildings if the mathematics center is large. In this stage, the architect will concern himself with room and space arrangements, traffic circulation in corridors, stairs, and elevators, the location and placement of toilet facilities, mechanical equipment spaces, etc. The broad general space relationships agreed upon in the schematic studies must be refined to assign each specific space-function to its location in the plan.

Areas related to a mathematics facility are: 1) instructional areas; 2) administrative headquarters and faculty offices; 3) library and other common use areas; 4) computation center and statistical laboratory; and 5) utility and service areas.

The architect must examine each of these areas

SCHEMATIC DESIGN STUDIES

ACCESS AND CIRCULATION

PHYSICAL ATTRIBUTES OF SITE

REGULATING AGENCIES

CLIMATE AND ORIENTATION

SOUND AND NOISE

THE PARKING PROBLEM

FIGURE 14

in detail, room by room, establish appropriate dimensions for each room, and then assign it to its proper place in the plan. At this time he must establish a basic space module that will accommodate the space needs as well as the structural, mechancial, and electrical systems. The establishment of a 4-foot module along the outer wall, for example, might involve changing a 26′ x 30′ classroom for 35 students (Fig. 22; see p. 64) to a slightly larger 28′ x 30′ classroom (Fig. 8a). Only then can he assemble the various units into an overall plan to produce a structure that is spatially adequate, aesthetically pleasing, and economically feasible.

Continued cooperation between the architect, the departmental planning director, and others responsible for the building is important in working out space allocations, to be sure that each space will not only be adequate in area but suitable in shape and general arrangement to satisfy the educational requirements. Some compromises may be necessary at this point, since economy of structure can impose certain restrictions, such as limitations on the floor and roof spans. Except for compelling reasons, the wishes of an individual or of a small group should not override the basic economy of establishing economic modules of construction components. If the usefulness of the space is seriously impaired, the architect may wish to replan the whole unit.

To complete his preliminary design study, the architect will usually prepare at this stage a simplified outline of the materials and finishes he proposes to use in developing his final working drawings and specifications. In establishing a standard of quality for the construction, he will need to consult at some length with those responsible for the maintenance and operation of the institution's physical plant. Local building codes and other regulations may fix certain minimum standards with respect to structural adequacy, fire safety, and health requirements; but there is still a wide range of choices to be made in regard to interior finishes, mechanical systems, lighting equipment, and other items, all of which will affect the construction cost. The architect must obtain a decision as to whether materials with a high initial cost but low maintenance costs or those of lower quality but higher upkeep are to be used. The funds appropriated for the project may predetermine the level of quality. Nevertheless, discussions on these factors should be undertaken in order that there be no misunderstandings later as to the reasons for the decisions.

When he presents his final preliminary drawings for approval, the architect may also present his preliminary estimate of the cost of the project. The architect is in no position to guarantee the exactness of his cost figures, since they are based on preliminary drawings prepared months and perhaps a year before actual bidding can take place. His cost estimates at this stage cannot be more than approximations drawn from his experience and judgment. Even the submitted bids of contractors, based on the final detailed drawings and specifications, may vary from 10 to 20 per cent, or even more, between low and high bids. Notwithstanding their tentative nature, these cost estimates of the architect, together with the preliminary drawings and outline specifications, should receive the most careful attention and critical appraisal, since the next stage of the project, in which the final detailed drawings are prepared, will be adversely affected by poor judgment in reviewing the preliminary studies.

C. FINAL WORKING DRAWINGS AND SPECIFICATIONS

The next step in the planning process is the preparation of final working drawings and specifications. These important documents are used by contractors in preparing their cost estimates, and also serve as contract documents for the construction of the building. Their preparation requires considerable care and adequate time—possibly eight to twelve months, as compared with three to four months spent on the preliminary stages of planning. Depending on the size and complexity of the project, a complete set of final working drawings for a mathematics building may comprise as few as 20 to 30 sheets of drawings or as many as 75 to 100. Covering the whole range of the various component parts of the building, these drawings are arranged for convenience into four identifiable groups: 1) architectural, 2) structural, 3) mechanical (plumbing, heating, ventilating, and air conditioning, etc.), and 4) electrical (power and lighting). In preparing his working drawings and specifications, the architect must consult with and coordinate the work of specialists in these and other fields, and he must satisfy the requirements of building codes.

The final specifications, which are to be considered complementary to the working drawings and not separate instruments, are likewise subdivided into sections covering the various building trades involved in the construction operation. Whereas the drawings give a graphic and highly technical representation of the building, indicating the materials of construction, the specifications prescribe with a high degree of precision the type and quality of materials to be used and the methods and procedures to be followed in achieving the desired result.

To complete this phase of his architectural service, the architect will generally assist and advise the owner in the taking of bids and the evaluation of the bid proposals and the qualifications of the bidders.

D. CONSTRUCTION The architect's responsibilities in this stage involve less effort on design and greater attention to administrative duties. As the owner's agent in matters relating to construction, the architect may be called upon to interpret the intent of the contract drawings and specifications.

Shop drawings are prepared by the various manufacturers for use in fabricating a particular product; these drawings deal only with the manufacturer's responsibility. The architect must check and either approve or correct hundreds of such shop drawings prepared by manufacturers of various component parts of the building, and he must coordinate the drawings of parts to be used in conjunction with each other. The architect must also inspect samples of various construction materials, checking them for type and quality to be sure that they meet the standards established in the specifications. To obtain a harmonious effect, the architect will select the exact colors, texture, and finish of the various materials, guided by a prearranged color schedule for each room.

At appropriate times during the construction the architect will certify to the owner that the contractor's requisitions for payment are reasonable and are properly due. He will submit to the owner any necessary change orders for revisions, additions, or deletions of work from the contract, due either to major or minor unforeseen causes. Funds should be set aside by the owner for such contingencies.

The supervision of the contractor's performance of contract in carrying out building operations is one of the more important duties of the architect during the construction phase. The architect gives directions in the resolution of problems that arise, and observes the work in progress himself to be sure that the terms of the contract are being honored and that the work is performed in accordance with the standards set by the specifications. The day-to-day inspection of work in progress is usually performed by a project inspector employed by the architect, often called the "clerk of works," whose salary is reimbursed to the architect by the owner.

During the entire construction period the architect keeps the owner informed as to the progress of the work. As the need arises, he will consult with him regarding the many and varied problems in every stage of construction. The closest cooperation between the contractor, the architect, and the owner is required to bring a construction project to a successful conclusion.

Beauty and light, sound and comfort

Six major factors must be considered in working out the details of a building design:

1. Spatial relations: size and relationship of building spaces.
2. Aesthetic value: the use of color and design to create an attractive and beautiful environment.
3. Visual environment: balanced lighting of chalkboards, desks, and work areas, and provision for darkening rooms if necessary.
4. Sonic control, within rooms and between them.
5. Cleaning, plumbing, and sanitation.
6. Thermal comfort: temperature and humidity control, and ventilation.

Inasmuch as the problems of spatial relations have already been discussed in some detail, we shall confine ourselves here to the other factors.

AESTHETIC CONSIDERATIONS Academic buildings and facilities should not only be functional; they should be objects of beauty in themselves, creating a pleasant environment in which to work. Beauty may be enhanced by an appropriate use of line and color in the design and furnishings. Carpeting may add to the beauty and comfort of an office or classroom and also save on heating and maintenance costs (see p. 132). Aesthetic considerations may even dictate a modification of internal arrangements, so that the exterior of the building shall present a balanced and pleasing appearance.

This is particularly true with respect to the size and arrangement of window openings, known as fenestration. Until recently the limitations of the masonry used in the structure imposed severe restrictions on the fenestration. Following the advent of the structural skeleton type of construction, in which the loads are supported by main structural supports of steel or concrete, and exterior walls serve only as surface covering, the window openings could be designed in any desired size or shape. New processes in the manufacture of glass have made available an almost limitless variety of glass sizes. A whole new array of materials for wall covering has also become available. These advances in structure and materials have opened up a new range of design solutions and expanded the architect's field of vision in designing the appearance of his buildings.

LIGHTING These new conditions soon led to a revised series of code regulations for school buildings, including restrictions on ceiling heights, room widths, and the ratio of glass area to room area. The basic premise was that classrooms could be lighted better by daylight alone, and that artificial illumination would be required only on cloudy days and in the evening. It soon became apparent that raw daylight was not an unmixed blessing and that some control over sunlight and glare was needed. Many forms of shades and blinds were used, as were many kinds of exterior shielding—overhangs, sunscreens, etc.—some with good results, many with poor results. Where proper controls have been designed into the building, there are a great many classrooms in use today with daylight as a principal source of illumination. These classrooms are providing a highly satisfactory visual environment for the students. There is a serious question, however, whether the cost of such control devices and special building design features can justify the belief in windows as the major lighting source for a schoolroom. The trend toward larger instructional areas, some divisible by folding partitions into smaller rooms, and the use of television and other visual aids, point to the use of electric light to provide the proper visual environment in the school building. Whether this trend away from dependence on outside light will continue all the way to windowless classrooms (Fig. 52) remains to be seen.

The new American Standard *Guide* for School Lighting,[1] published in April 1962, replaces the 1948 American Standard *Practice* for School Lighting, which for years has been the standard handbook for all school lighting. It should be noted at once that the one-word change in title is indeed a significant change and reflects the concern of those involved in its preparation with the need for a more flexible approach to school lighting than can be achieved by a rigid set of standards. The *Guide* itself no longer specifies the foot-candle requirements for given schoolroom tasks, but rather indicates the wide range of choices within which architects and engineers can create efficient lighting systems. New information is given on the effects of glare, both direct and reflected—a most important contribution to proper seeing conditions (Fig. 59). In essence, the *Guide* emphasizes lighting "quality" over "quantity" and admirably defines, in simple terms, the cardinal principles of good school lighting.

In discussing natural lighting, the *Guide* gives some attention to the control of outside brightnesses and discusses a fairly new technique in the use of light-absorbing or low-transmission neutral glass. This glass, which is transparent, and should be nondistorting, serves somewhat the same purpose as sun-glasses do for the wearer, by bringing the outside brightnesses more into balance with the room and task brightnesses.

Of particular interest to the mathematician is the attention given in the *Guide* to the matter of chalkboards and their lighting (see p. 137). Serious consideration should be given to the use of supplementary lighting at all chalkboard installations in mathematics classrooms.

SONIC CONSIDERATIONS The science of acoustics is a relative newcomer to the field of building design and construction. Perhaps this is due to the fact that a number of our sound problems today were not present in many of the older, more massive buildings of yesterday. The light-weight floor and wall systems in our modern buildings, the increased use of glass—both exterior and interior—plus the complex systems of ducts, cables, and motors found in almost every new building, all contribute to the noise-making potential with which the architect must now deal.

In making provision for good acoustic conditions within a room or building, we must take into account two separate facets of the sound problem: control of sound within the room; and exclusion of noise from sources outside the room.

The control of sound within a fixed room is a relatively simple matter, since there is available a whole range of acoustic materials that absorb sound. However, sound control is overdone when sound absorption is raised to the point where a room becomes acoustically "dead," and where speech becomes unintelligible at short distances. Ideally, then, proper acoustics within a given room calls for appropriate amounts of hard and soft surfaces. Arriving at the proper solution is somewhat more complex when room spaces are made flexible in size, using folding partitions, so that several small rooms may be changed into a single large room. These special problems may require the services of an acoustical consultant. Whether or not a consultant is engaged, the problem cannot be ignored, since the correction of a bad acoustic condition can be inordinately more costly than adequate initial accommodation.

Preventing the entrance of noise created outside the room is a somewhat more difficult task.[18] Space allocations which place noisy activities as far from quiet study areas as possible will accomplish a great deal. Such allocations should be a matter of first concern to the architect. The most effective barrier to sound transmission is mass; the thicker and more solid the material, the better. The solid masonry walls and partitions of yesterday were a prime reason for the small number of sound transmission problems in our older schools. Partly because of thinner, lighter partitions and walls, our newer buildings require considerably more care in isolating sound; but this is also because sound transmission from room to room can follow many paths—through ventilating ducts and piping, over ceilings, and under and around doors and windows. Care in the placement of piping, lining of ducts with absorbent liners, sealing spaces around and above partitions, locating machinery and equipment in a remote space—all of these will help reduce the transmission of sound. It might be well to note here that a certain amount of background noise or general hum can be tolerated in most instructional areas. In fact, the absence of outside noises can make small noises within a room—a clock ticking—just as distracting to the occupant as would a low-level hum of outside noises.

In the design of large lecture halls and auditoriums, acoustical implications should be kept in mind at the time the initial architectural treatment of the room is being considered. In other words, a proper shape of the room may help more to accomplish good acoustical surroundings than will the application of surface treatments to compensate for an inherently poor acoustical design. The size and shape of the room, and even the height of the ceiling, can affect the hearing characteristics to a marked degree. So, too, can the choice of seating material and floor covering appreciably affect the acoustical calculations. It is also well to determine at an early stage whether or not seats will be upholstered, and whether the floor will be carpeted or covered with resilient floor tile.

Rooms designed to house a number of desk calculators should be given special acoustical treatment to subdue machine noises, both for the room occupants and those in adjacent areas. Similarly, rooms for computers and auxiliary equipment need specialized acoustical design and treatment.

PLUMBING Plumbing and sanitary requirements for mathematics facilities differ little from those of other typical academic buildings. Local and state codes usually govern both the number of fixtures required and the method of installation. Unfortunately, there is no uniform pattern across the country that establishes the ratio of fixtures to occupants. Consequently, plumbing costs can vary widely.

An excellent report on "Plumbing Fixture Requirements in University Instructional and Research Buildings" has been published by University Facilities Research Center in cooperation with the Educational Facilities Laboratories.[43] The research on which this report is based indicates that a study of actual fixture use, as opposed to code requirements, would make it appear that these building types are generally overfixtured. Apparently, considerably more money than necessary is being spent on toilet facilities and plumbing. Toilet rooms and their plumbing installations are among the most expensive areas, per square foot of space, in the typical instructional building. These occupy about 2.5 per cent of the net area of college buildings, but plumbing costs involve from 3.5 to 12 per cent of total construction costs.[43] Any excess in the number or size of fixtures can absorb funds needed for other more important uses.

In selecting the sizes and locations of toilet rooms, the architect should consider room utilization and traffic patterns in the building. Larger toilet rooms should be placed where the use will be greatest—for example, near the main corridors and on the main floor. Public use areas, such as lobbies, auditoriums, and lecture halls, should be serviced by facilities capable of accommodating a large crowd in a short time. Plumbing costs will be reduced if these toilets can be so located that they are used not only for special functions, but also for the regular functions of the building.

Drinking water should be provided at various

places throughout the building, generally in corridors and public areas. It should be noted that the conventional drinking fountain is tending more and more to be replaced by electric water coolers. For both kinds it is better to use the wall-hung type fixture than the floor pedestal type, and to set it in a niche or recess if possible.

While no particular plumbing fixture requirements are necessary in mathematics classrooms, it is interesting to note that most European university classrooms for mathematics are equipped with a small wash basin in the room, for handwashing and chalkboard cleaning. The advantages of this amenity are obvious and should, perhaps, be adopted in this country. Workrooms, duplicating rooms, and other such facilities, should obviously make provision for handwashing. Custodians' closets require special utility sinks, preferably of the floor-sink type, which allow for filling and emptying mop-pails and scrub-buckets without the need for lifting.

HEATING AND VENTILATING The requirements for heating and ventilating academic buildings vary widely because of geographic location and local code regulations. Satisfactory systems can be designed with coal, gas, oil, or electricity as the heating fuel, and with steam, hot water, or tempered air for distributing heat. The choice of fuel will depend on availability and relative cost. The choice of heating system is a technical problem for the architect and his mechanical engineers, working with the campus maintenance personnel.

Provision must be made, in designing a new facility, for both present and future requirements. Heating and ventilating systems based on a rigid design for meeting present requirements may be extremely expensive to adapt to future changes in the arrangement of rooms and partitions. Rather than using a system based on a room-by-room analysis of heating and ventilating loads, it may be desirable to use a modular system. This means treating each floor of the building as if it were an open loft, without regard to partitioning, and arranging heating and ventilating units to serve each half or quarter structural bay. This approach ensures that the necessary heating and ventilating capacity will service almost any arrangement of rooms and partitions, with a minimum of alteration or adjustment. The extra expense of ductwork and equipment for the modular system is justified by its long-range flexibility.

Consideration should be given in the design stage to the need for providing adequate zoning of the heating and ventilating systems. It is well to control certain areas of the building independently of each other. For example, instructional areas, administrative offices, auditoriums, and the computation center are elements that may require the mechanical systems to be in operation at times when the rest of the building is not in use. Within such areas, of course, it will be necessary to provide enough local temperature control devices to regulate thermal conditions of individual rooms and spaces. It is true that highly refined and responsive control systems are expensive and can increase heating and ventilating installation costs disproportionately; but the alternative is often a discomforting overheating of some individual rooms and underheating of others, when groups of rooms are under the control of one thermostatic control device.

AIR CONDITIONING In discussions relating to the design of educational facilities, the question of air conditioning is bound to be brought up at some stage. Obviously, the sooner this question is raised the better, and the answer should be given only after careful consideration of all the pertinent factors.[18] If, as appears likely, educational institutions are to be faced with not only a longer school year but also a longer school day, then in those areas where climate is a factor air conditioning becomes not only desirable but necessary.

Architects are seriously concerned with this matter, since they understand the problems of installing cooling systems at a later date. In fact, a great many architects are designing their new educational buildings in such a way that it will be necessary later merely to install the cooling equipment. They feel that the extra cost of providing the additional space and ductwork now will pay dividends in the future. Most architects feel that air conditioning (cooling) will eventually become as much a matter of course in buildings as heating is now. It would be well for any institution to evaluate the difference in cost between the required heating and ventilating system proposed for the building and a complete year-round air-conditioning system. If the ventilating system is at all complex, perhaps little additional cost would be involved to obtain air conditioning in the initial construction. Furthermore, if a computation center with its fairly rigid temperature and humidity control requirements is part of the contemplated project, then consideration of air conditioning is all the more justified. Certainly, if air conditioning makes a significant contribution to the effectiveness of the work of the faculty and students who use the building, it is not merely a luxury and will more than pay for itself in productivity.

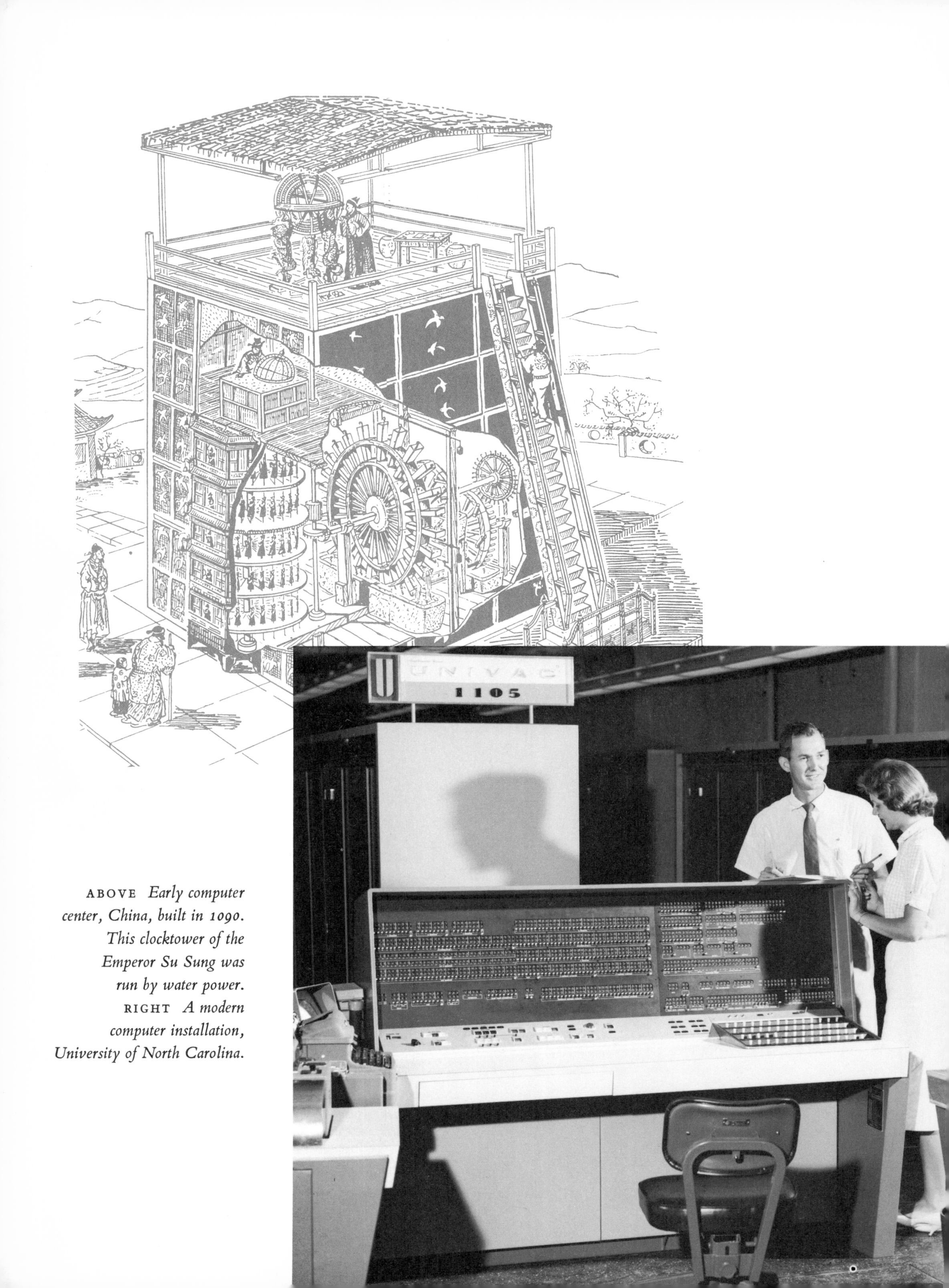

ABOVE *Early computer center, China, built in 1090. This clocktower of the Emperor Su Sung was run by water power.* RIGHT *A modern computer installation, University of North Carolina.*

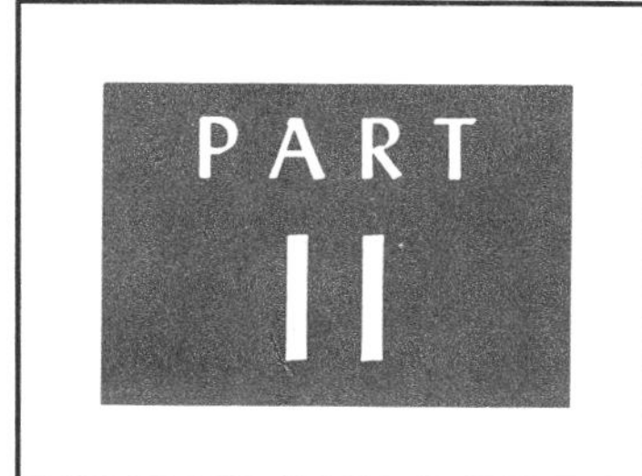

SPECIAL CONSIDERATIONS IN PLANNING FACILITIES FOR THE MATHEMATICAL SCIENCES IN HIGHER EDUCATION

Part Two presents detailed considerations involved in planning instructional areas, study and research areas, administrative and public areas, and departmental libraries for the mathematical sciences. Part Two also examines the growth, organization, function, location, and protection of the modern computation center, and analyzes the various areas and facilities required.

4 INSTRUCTIONAL AREAS

Large group instruction – Lecture rooms and auditoriums

The problem of facilities for instruction in mathematics and statistics has several important aspects. One is to design and provide the best standard classroom for a typical class of 20 to 30 students, with adequate blackboards, lighting, heating, ventilation, and soundproofing, and wired to display a synchronized clock and to accommodate slide projectors, overhead projectors, television, or other electrical equipment. Another is to plan for spaces for individualized study and work, such as the tables equipped with desk calculators in a statistical laboratory, or individualized study cubicles for future use in programed instruction, possibly similar to the cubicles in a language laboratory. These and related problems of equipment will be considered in later sections.

The major problem to be treated in this section is the problem of describing facilities for teaching mathematics in a college or university to medium-sized (36–100) and large-sized (over 100) groups of students. It was mentioned on page 8 that enrollments in mathematics and statistics in U. S. colleges and universities are expected to more than double between 1960 and 1970, but that only a moderate increase (possibly between 25 and 50 per cent) in trained college and university teachers of these subjects appears likely for the country as a whole in this decade. It was also mentioned in discussing the project questionnaire that about 35 per cent of the mathematics departments reporting were teaching the subject in some classes larger than 40, and that 12 per cent had at least one class larger than 100. As enrollments increase more rapidly than the teacher supply, more students will be taught mathematics and statistics in medium-sized or large groups than in the past. An important question is whether the traditional class sizes of 20 or 30 should be allowed to creep up to 35, 40, or 50 as enrollments increase, or whether there is an objective basis for arriving at some maximum size above which teachers and administrators will agree that the advantages of small group instruction are lost. If classes of 50 or 150 are considered equally impersonal, the larger size may be considered preferable for a variety of reasons. A decision on optimum class sizes in view of the staff, budget, and enrollment has important implications in the planning of facilities.

Apart from the size of existing classrooms on a given campus, what are the issues involved in the size of mathematics classes? One element is personal. An instructor may feel that he should talk to individuals and that individuals should be able to talk to him. But the upper bound of size at which individuals amalgamate into a crowd may be 20 for one instructor and 100 for another. Some can call every student by name in a class of 60 after six or eight class meetings; others cannot do so in a class of 30 at the end of the term. Some have voices that can be heard without loud speakers in a class of 500; others are hard to hear in a class of 35. So it will be best to plan for classrooms of a variety of sizes for different types of courses and levels of instruction.

The new mathematics building at the University of Wisconsin will include an assortment of classrooms seating from 30 to 60, two lecture rooms for 100, and one auditorium for 300. The new mathematics building at Dartmouth College has a lecture room for 200 with excellent acoustics (Fig. 15), sloping floors rising about three inches per row, staggered seats, overhead projector, and a projection booth in the back; class sizes between 20 and 100 are mostly avoided as being too large for personal contact and too small for efficiency. The new circular classroom and office building housing the mathematics department at

FIGURE 15 *Lecture room of mathematics building, Dartmouth College*

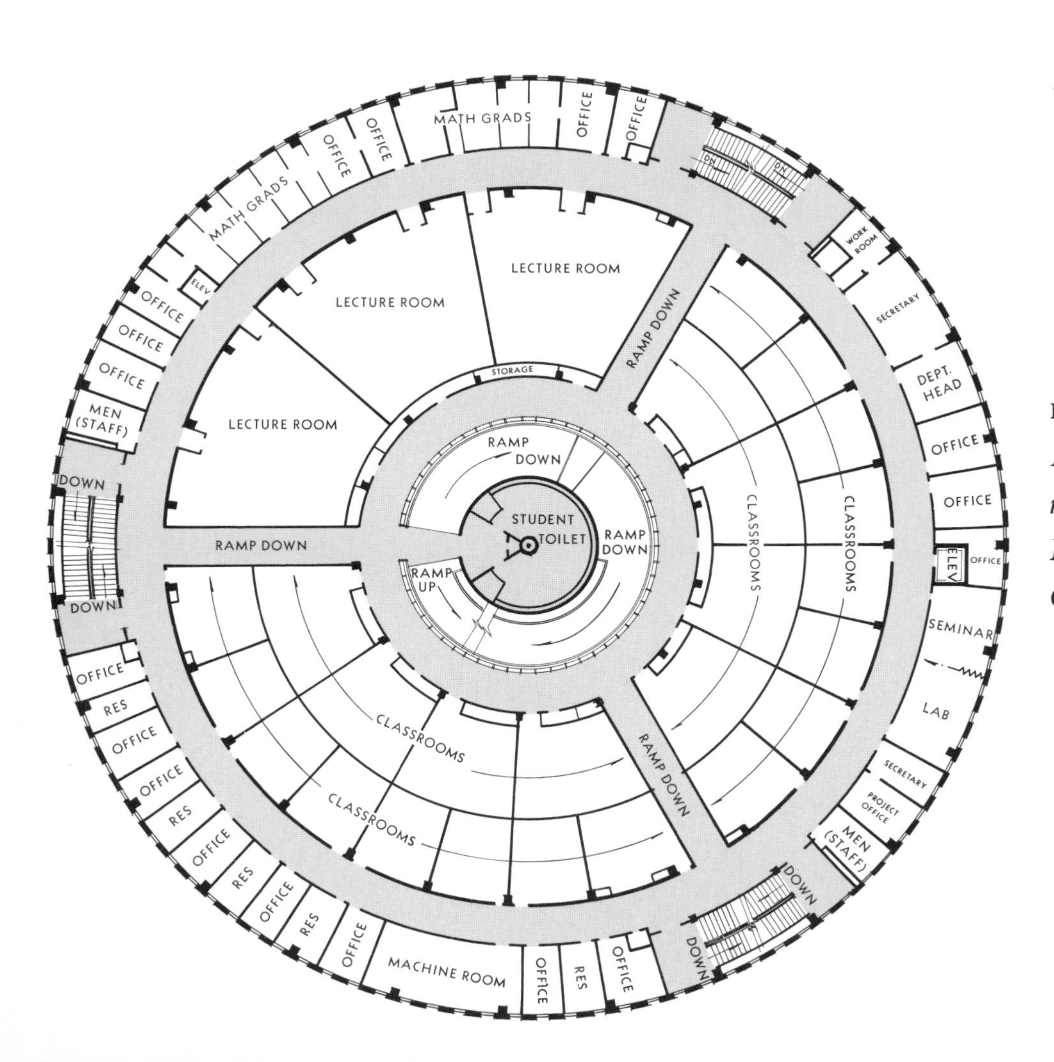

FIGURE 16
Plan of third floor mathematics facilities, North Carolina State College, Raleigh

FIGURE 17 *Plan of building in Figure 18, Cerritos College*

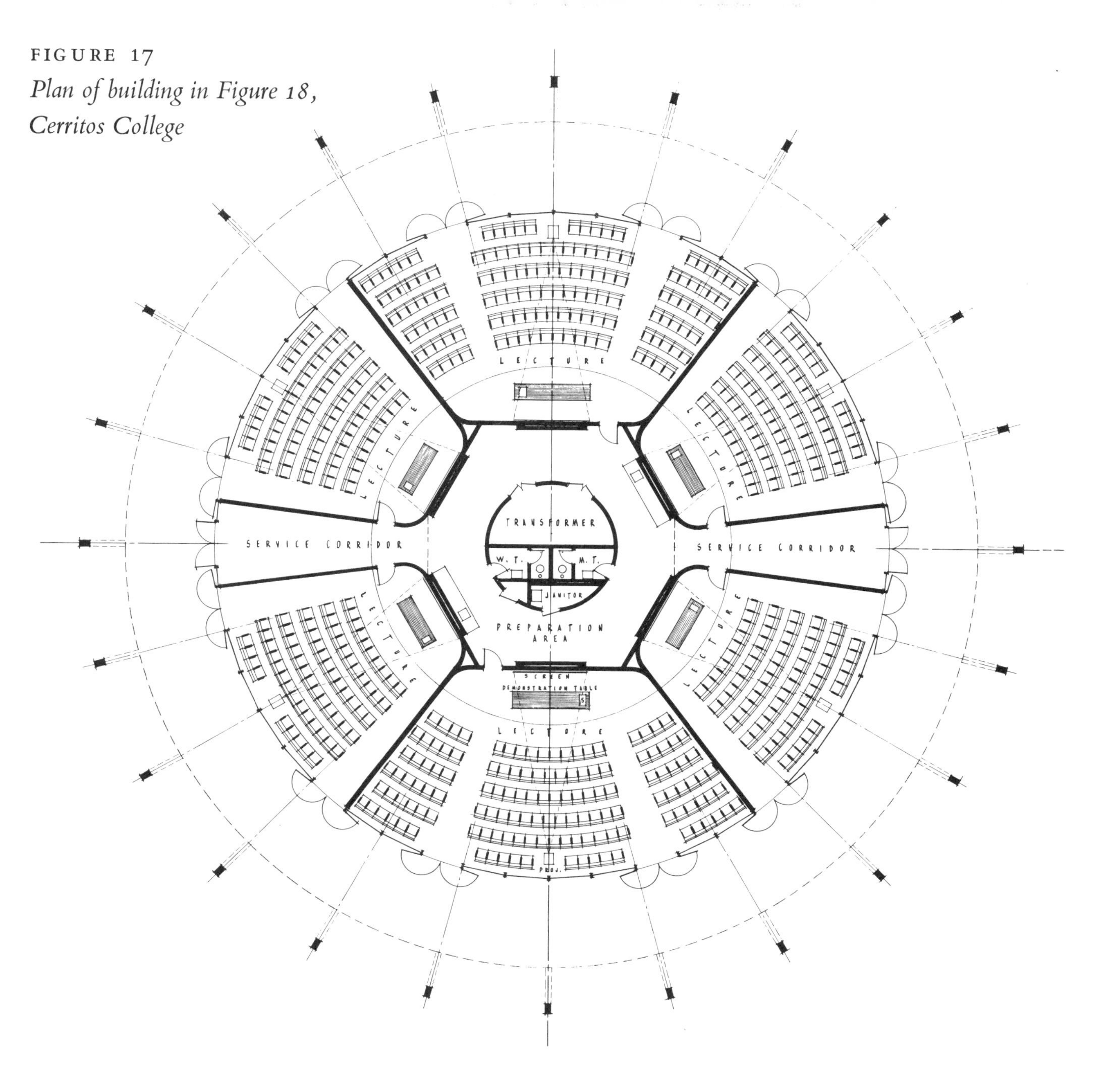

FIGURE 18 *Circular auditorium building, Cerritos College, Norwalk, California*

North Carolina State College includes three large lecture rooms with sloping floors, two seating 110, and the third 190. These three lecture rooms together share a 120-degree sector between an outer circular office and classroom corridor and an inner circular classroom corridor at a slightly lower level, entered by students from an inner helical ramp (Fig. 16).

At Cerritos College near Los Angeles, a circular auditorium building (Figs. 17, 18) contains six lecture halls with sloping floors, four with 65 seats, and two with 130 seats, arranged so that students may enter directly from the outside and teachers may enter from the central core that contains storage areas, toilets, and a teachers' room. Each classroom has only six rows of seats and gives the lecturer a pleasant feeling of being close to his class. However, a few seats at the extreme right and left of the large auditoriums (Fig. 19) might have to be avoided in a mathematics class because of the difficulty of viewing the front chalkboard.

Some teachers experienced with large lectures support them not from grim necessity but because of positive advantages. (In Germany and Denmark, an elementary mathematics course is seldom split into parallel sections unless the enrollment exceeds the capacity of available large lecture rooms seating several hundred.) The large lecture provides substantial economy in teaching —one factor in obtaining lower teaching hours

FIGURE 19 *Auditorium for 130 students, in the building of Figures 17, 18*

and higher salaries for the staff. Next, in large lectures there is positive control over the content of examinations—questions on a common examination are not restricted to the sometimes rather small common content of the material taught in various parallel sections by less experienced instructors or assistants. Assistants connected with a large lecture are paced in their teaching of related recitation sections and are more easily supervised and trained professionally. Also, each student in the course has the opportunity for some intellectual contact with one of the more effective and willing lecturers on the staff, chosen for this assignment.

Clearly, a lecture room should be so placed in a building that it is accessible to students without overcrowding of corridors or stairways. Coat racks, adequate bulletin boards lining the corridors, and ample toilet facilities should be provided nearby. Close proximity to faculty offices should be avoided (p. 74). Two or more lecture rooms adjacent to each other provide an excellent facility for national and regional scientific meetings scheduling parallel sessions for talks.

The room itself should be arranged so that the audience can see well, hear well, and be comfortable. In part this depends on temperature, humidity, background of light and sound, seating space, and other features which, though significant, are not peculiar to the teaching of mathematics. A teacher or the presiding officer at a lecture should not have to choose between stifling discomfort and noisy air conditioning that interferes with the lecture; noiseless air conditioning does exist. But here we are concerned with matters more specifically connected with mathematics teaching.

Chalkboards are the most important visual aid for the mathematician. Since the mathematics department rarely schedules enough large classes to justify exclusive use of a large lecture room, it often must share one with other departments. A standard complaint of mathematics lecturers who use a shared facility is lack of adequate good-quality chalkboard at the front of the room. A detailed discussion of chalkboards and chalk will be presented in Part IV (p. 137).

PROJECTION SYSTEMS The large lecture room should be built to accommodate a variety of projection systems that may be used immediately or in the more distant future. An overhead projector requires an electrical outlet near the lecturer's table, placed so that the lecturer will not trip over the cord, and also a screen properly mounted to assure that the entire class has good visibility with minimum distortion. More screens or a wide screen may be needed to enable the lecturer to use two or more overhead projectors at once. If movies, films, or slides are projected from the rear of the room and reflected from a front screen, the room should have a projection booth, or at least a suitable stand and electrical outlet for the projector. Remote controls for operating the projector are desirable. Shades may be required for darkening a room with windows. If the recently developed "rear screen" method of projection is to be used (Fig. 65), in which the image is thrown onto a translucent screen mounted in the front wall from a projector in an adjacent room beyond the front wall, the building plans must include adequate provision for this projection room. Furthermore, the translucent screen should be built into the front wall in a position where it can be seen well but where its presence will not obstruct the use of an adequate vertically rising chalkboard. Provision for receiving and transmitting television is also an important consideration in planning a lecture room for large group instruction. A more detailed study of the various facilities needed for these projection systems is included in Part IV.

A room or space for the preparation of transparencies or other visuals is a corollary of their use. Material can be prepared on ordinary paper and copied quickly onto a transparency by a thermal duplicator or similar equipment. Such copies can be posted after the lecture for inspection by students. Storage for such materials must also be provided, as well as for any materials distributed to students to supplement their lecture notes. It has been suggested that the partitioning of a large storage room into wire cages provides a flexible means for sharing storage space.

SEATING AND VISIBILITY Good visibility depends not only on the arrangement of chalkboards and of projection screens and equipment, but also to a large degree upon seating arrangements. Factors to be considered are avoidance of obstructions, slope of the floor and height of the speaker's platform, viewing distance, and the extreme vertical and horizontal viewing angles. It is clear that a good lecture room will not have columns or supports so placed as to block the front screen and chalkboard from any seat in the room. However, when a large demonstration table stands on a platform between the chalkboard and the audience, the lower 12 to 18 inches of the board often cannot be seen by people in the first few rows. In this case, vertically sliding chalkboards are needed so that the writing may be raised to a level where it can be seen by all. A sloping floor in a lecture room will generally add somewhat to the cost of construction, but in many instances it will be worth the extra cost in providing good visibility for all. The object of a sloping floor is to make it easier for a person to see over or around the heads of those in front of him and to give the impression of a smaller room. If the seats in successive rows are staggered so that the line of sight from one seat to the lecturer goes directly between the centers of two seats in the next row, the rise required per row may be reduced by half. Closely interdependent are the slope of the floor and the height of the speaker's platform. The use of a raised platform for the teacher has advantages in increased visibility in any room seating more than about 40 persons, provided that the table or other furniture on the platform does not block the chalkboard for those in the front rows.

Studies of distances and angles for satisfactory viewing indicate that seats should be placed at a distance from a screen not less than twice nor more than six times the width of the screen image to be viewed and that the distance from a person to the chalkboard should not exceed 400 times the size of the smallest letter or digit being written. Thus, if the back row of students is 64 feet away, the lecturer should make his letters and digits at least two inches high. Similar studies indicate that the angle of elevation from the eye to the upper part of an object on the screen or chalkboard should not exceed 30 degrees (see Fig. 20). If lecture rooms are built in a fan shape instead of a rectangular shape, the minimum angle between line of sight and the blackboard should be at least 30 degrees and preferably more than 45 degrees. These limitations of viewing distance and angle impose restrictions on the placement of seats for adequate viewing. A detailed analysis of viewing distances and angles is given in the Rensselaer Polytechnic Institute research report entitled "New Spaces for Learning."[36]

ACOUSTICAL CONSIDERATIONS Appropriate acoustical treatment is essential in a large lecture room. Lecture rooms have been designed for 200 or more students in which not only the lecturer but a student asking a question from his seat in a clear voice can be heard well in all parts of the room. There are also rooms for less than 100 students in which neither the lecturer nor the students can be clearly heard. Good acoustical treatment and good visibility in a lecture room permit it to be used effectively for large groups at a considerable saving in instructional cost. Any economy that results in poor acoustics is not a genuine economy at all.

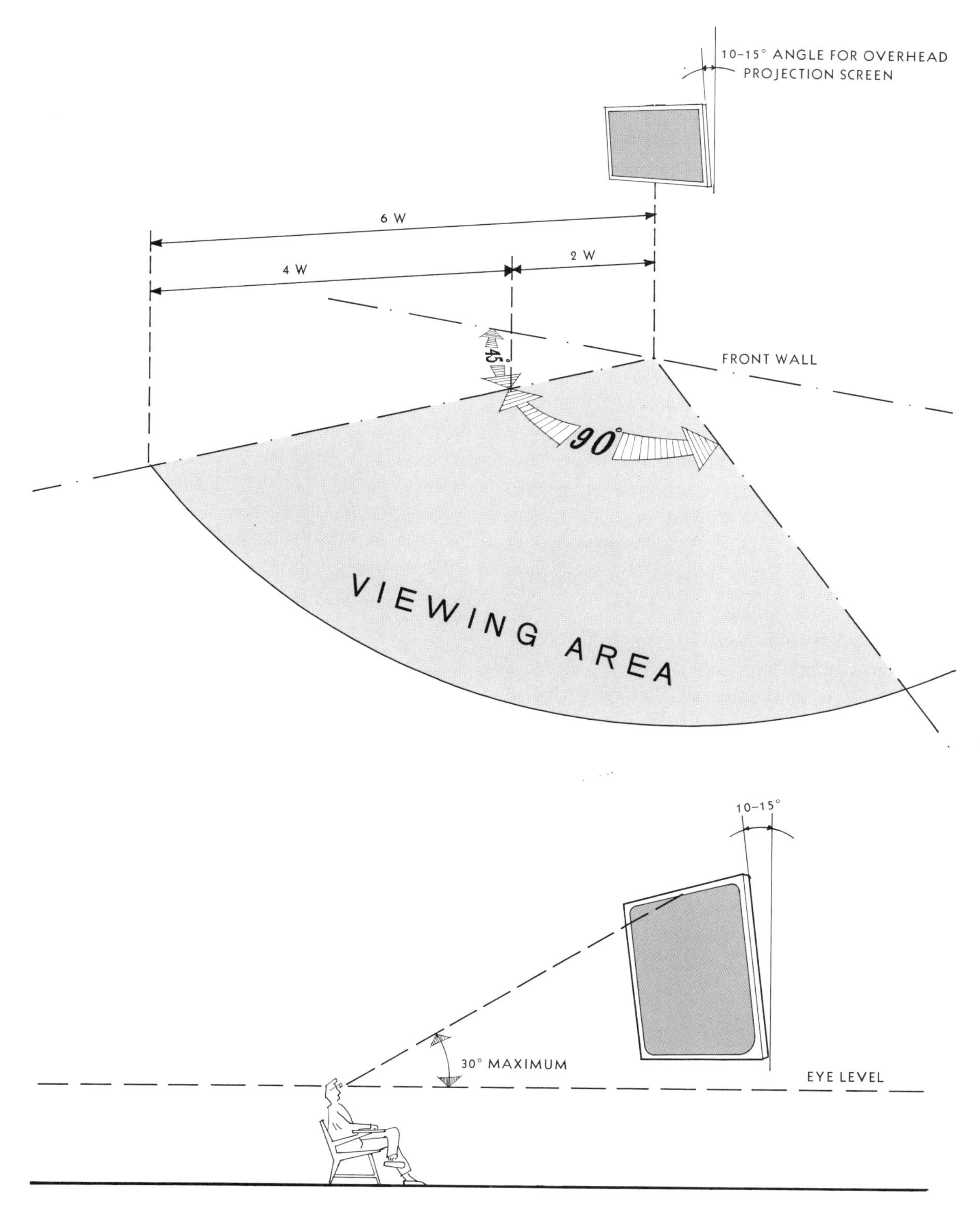

FIGURE 20 *Optimum viewing angles*

The acoustical properties of an auditorium depend on the number of people present. One way to increase sound absorption in an existing large room at a time when many seats are empty is to provide a panel of acoustic tile fastened under each seat. This is particularly effective on seats that spring back when empty.

A sound amplification system may be necessary when the audience exceeds a certain critical size. This critical size is not absolute but depends both on the acoustics of the room and the voice of the speaker. Some rooms seating 400 people require no amplification system for a speaker with a resonant voice. In others seating less than 100 there are many spots where even an exceptionally good speaker cannot be distinctly heard. The experience of some high school teachers who use a large lecture room for team teaching is that voice projection to more than 125 students is too tiring without amplification. Most lecture rooms seating more than 150 to 200 people should be equipped with a sound amplification system, and smaller rooms may require this unless their acoustical properties are exceptional. Speaker units can be placed at appropriate intervals in the ceiling or walls. However, the usual fixed microphone or even the neck microphone creates a problem for the typical mathematics lecturer. Unless he is presenting his lecture from a fixed position by an overhead projector, the mathematician likes to walk as he talks and writes on the chalkboard. He does not like to be tied to a lectern, or to find himself tripping over a cord of wire. His problem may be solved by using a cordless microphone transmitter which communicates with a receiver amplifier at radio frequency. Good ones are available at moderate cost.

DIVISIBLE AUDITORIUMS A problem in efficient space utilization arises if a large class scheduled as a large lecture section two or three days per week is to be broken up into a number of small sections on certain other days. Typically, the large lecture room remains vacant at the assigned hour on days when the small sections are scheduled, and it is hard to obtain an adequate number of classrooms at convenient hours. A properly designed lecture room may help to solve the problem, if it can be subdivided by operable partitions into two or three small group areas acoustically insulated from each other and equipped with adequate chalkboard (Fig. 21).[16]

Classrooms

The project questionnaire indicated that the large majority of students in mathematics are taught in classes of 20–29 students, and most of the respondents felt this was the ideal size for mathematics classes. Instruction to groups of this size can still be personalized instruction; it gives adequate opportunity for the teacher to know his students individually and for the students to ask and respond to questions in class. Part of the class period may be spent in the formal presentation of the mathematical theory or the illustration of this theory by examples. For this work the typical mathematics instructor wants a large area of chalkboard space at the front of the room. Some would like to be able to write steadily for 50 minutes without erasing. On the other hand, some teachers supplement their formal presentation by having the students do problems at the board. These teachers would like to have a whole class of 25 students go to the board at once. To allow 3 feet of board space per student, this teacher would require 75 feet of board space around the room.

Major factors to be considered in designing a classroom are the following:

1 Seating and writing surfaces
2 Space and furnishings for the lecturer
3 The use of wall space, including chalkboards, screens, size and location of windows, etc.

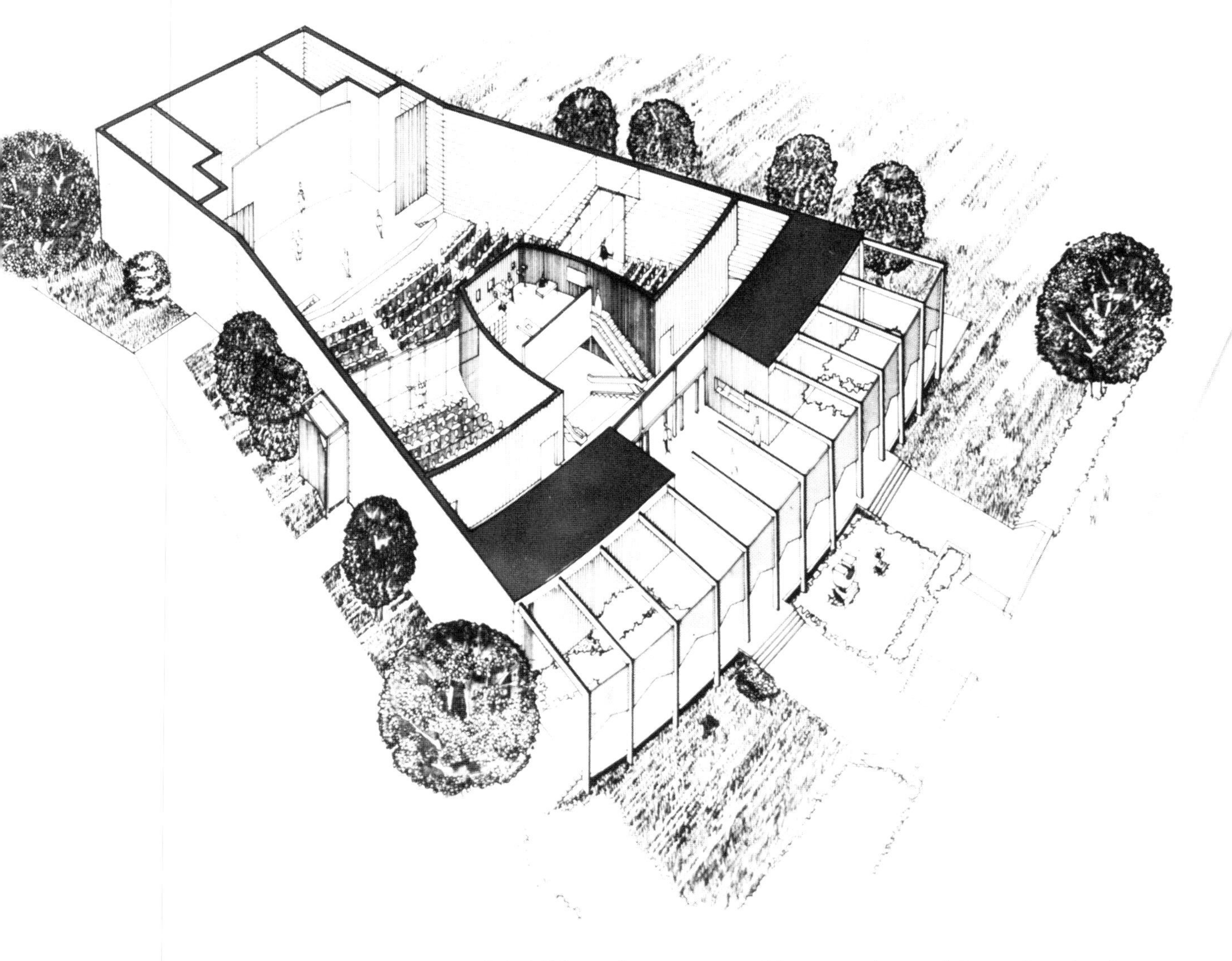

FIGURE 21 *Divisible auditorium, Boulder City (Nevada) High School*

4 Facilities for projection and television
5 Coat racks, storage, and other conveniences
6 Acoustics and lighting
7 Heating and air conditioning
8 Aesthetic considerations

CLASSROOM SEATING The seating arrangement is the most important feature in determining the size and shape of a classroom. Seating arrangements in a mathematics classroom should provide all students with a good view of the front chalkboard, ready access both to the seats and to chalkboards on other walls, an adequate, well-illuminated writing surface at each seat, a place to set books and papers, reasonable comfort, and privacy in taking examinations. In a mathematics class of 50 or fewer students, where a long front chalkboard is desirable, it seems better to have the front wall longer than the side walls. This presupposes that there are more students in a row of seats than there are rows; for example, visibility is better in a classroom having five rows of seven seats than in one having seven rows of five seats. In a room measuring 26′ × 30′ (Fig. 22), with separate tablet armchairs for 35 students, the seven seats in a row might have a spacing of 3′6″ between seat centers laterally and 4′6″ between the end seat centers and side walls (6 × 3′6″ + 9′ = 30′). Spacing from front to back in a column might be 3 feet between seat centers with 4 feet behind the back seat center and 10 feet between the front-seat center and the front chalkboard (4 × 3′ + 14′ = 26′). This pattern allows for aisles of about 20 inches between columns, a width just under the 22-inch "unit width" used as a standard in estimating the number of persons who can walk abreast in a corridor or stairhall.[25] This arrangement requires about 22 square feet of space per student. Lecture halls whose seats have folding tablet arms may allow 15 square feet or less per student.

Close-packed seating arrangements are not the most desirable, but sometimes are necessary because larger rooms are not available. Laws in some states provide that no person shall have to pass more than six others to reach an aisle; hence 14 persons in a row between aisles is an absolute maximum. If 10 to 14 students sit next to each other in a row behind a long strip table or writing ledge, the ledge should be at least 12 inches wide and should provide at least 2 feet of length per person. An arrangement whereby the nearer half of the writing surface in front of each person can fold up and away from the writer gives more room for students to pass. A spacing between rows of 42 inches between seat centers is adequate for most seating arrangements that use strip tables for writing.

Tablet armchairs are commonly used for seating in college classrooms in the United States and permit rows to be spaced every 3 feet. They are satisfactory for most mathematics classes that do not make use of special equipment (such as desk calculators or slide rules), provided they have a large writing surface and a shelf underneath for

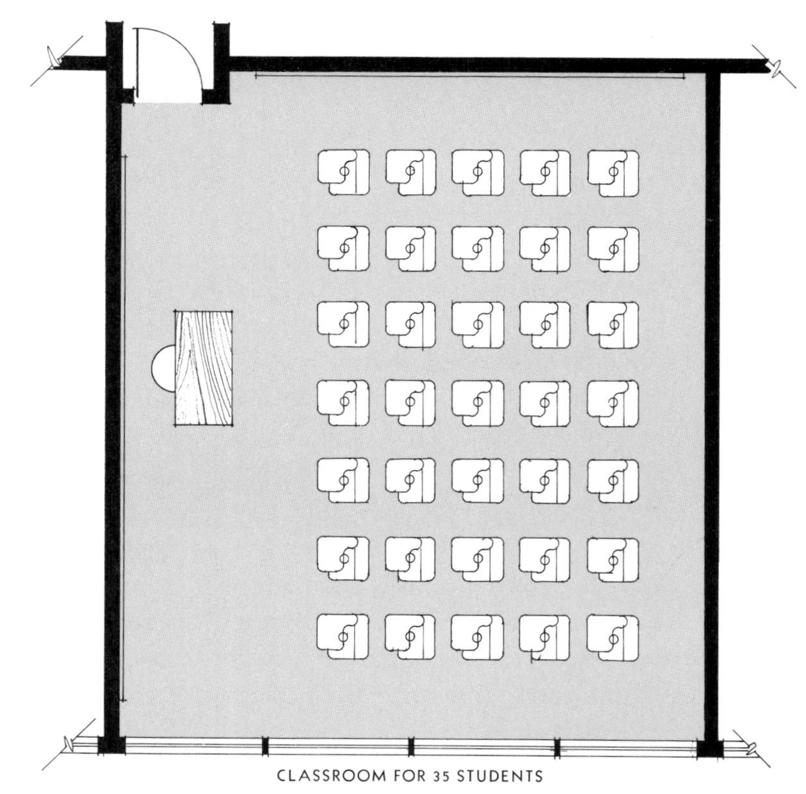

FIGURE 22

Seating arrangement in a classroom for 35 students

FIGURE 23 *Classroom seating 45. 113 Fine Hall, Princeton University*

books and papers. Tablet armchairs may be found either fixed to the floor, fastened together in sets of two to six that can be moved as a group, or individually movable. When chairs are fixed to the floor the arrangement should be one that permits good visibility and ready access. Good visibility may be achieved in three ways: by sloping the floor, by staggering seats in consecutive rows, or by wide spacing. A very popular classroom in Fine Hall at Princeton University (Fig. 23) measures 24′ × 24′ and seats 45 students compactly in five rows of nine adjacent fixed tablet armchairs, with 26-inch spacing laterally between seat centers on a sloping floor that drops 10 or 12 inches from back to front; the rows have 37-inch spacing between seat centers; all students have a good view of the three double panels of vertically sliding chalkboard that completely cover the front wall. The lecturer's platform is at the same level as the floor at the rear of the room. There are no central aisles. One side wall has an additional 12-foot panel of chalkboard. Given an additional width of 4 feet, student access to the seats would be improved in this room if the nine seats in a row were separated into sets of three seats by two 2-foot wide aisles. With such an arrangement a class of 30 could use the room for examinations without needing the middle seat in each triple, and thus without having any two students next to each other. On the other hand, for a slightly larger class of 36, the middle seats in each triple could be used only in the front two rows, where the teacher could readily observe the students. An arrangement permitting a class of 30 to spread out for examination purposes in a 26′ × 26′ classroom seating 40 students would be the following (Fig. 24): in each of five rows, spaced 3 feet apart from front to back between seat centers, let two triples of seats be placed with seat centers 2 feet apart laterally and with a 4-foot central aisle from front to back between triples. In 5-foot aisles at the sides, let movable tablet armchairs be placed next to the fixed seats for lectures and recitations (keeping the 3-foot aisle by the walls), but let these chairs be moved over next to the walls during examinations. If the center chair in each fixed

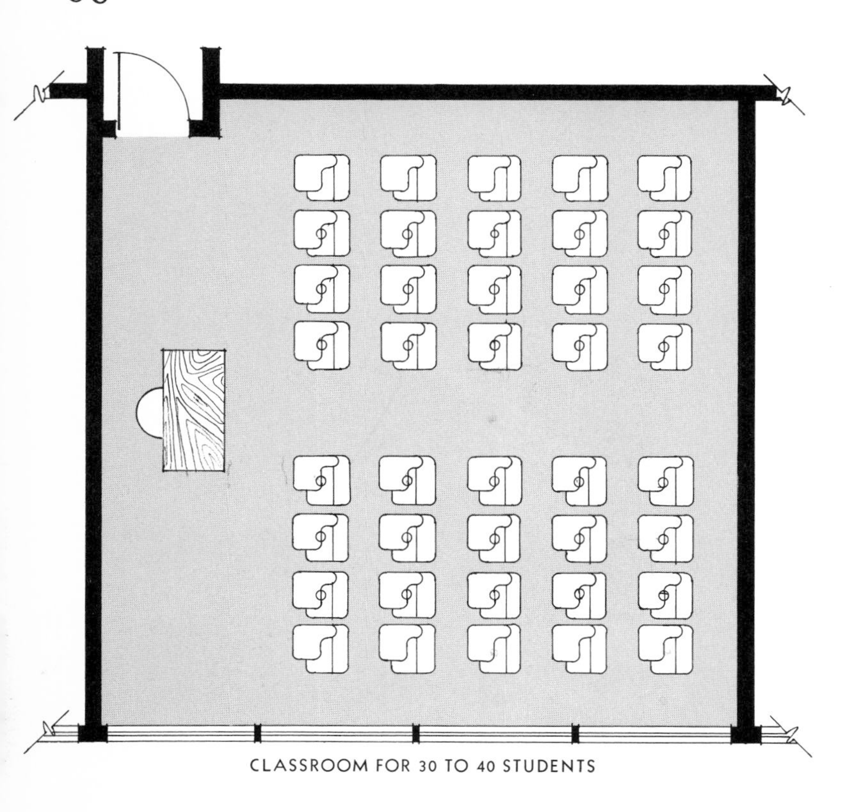

FIGURE 24 *Classroom for 40, with 10 side seats movable*

triple were left vacant, there would still be 30 widely spaced chairs available for an examination.

A FRONT PLATFORM In front of the students' seating area, there should be enough space for the lecturer to walk back and forth before a long chalkboard. In rooms with more than five rows of seats there is an advantage in having a platform, possibly 8 inches above the floor and extending the full width of the room, on which the teacher may walk the length of the board without danger of falling off the end. The chalkboard should then be raised correspondingly higher above the classroom floor for better visibility. The mathematics teacher needs a table on which he can place his lecture notes and papers, but it is better to have this table either movable on casters or fixed at the side of the platform where it does not block the view of the chalkboard from the first two rows of students. If an overhead projector is to be used, there must either be a place where it can be mounted permanently at the front of the room, or there must be provision for rolling it in on a cart and connecting it electrically. In the latter case, the front platform might be slightly lower and be accessible by a ramp. The mathematics teacher seldom sits during a lecture but may wish to sit down during an examination. There should be a chair by his table or desk.

A WASH BASIN Chalkdust on the clothes should not be the trademark of a teacher. In new mathematics institutes in Germany, the standard procedure is to supply a small wash basin next to the chalkboard in each classroom and office. Chalkboards there are commonly wiped with a damp cloth or sponge instead of a dusty eraser. However, some chalkboards used in the United States are damaged by water. Frequent cleaning of erasers, possibly by a special vacuum cleaner designed for this purpose, can reduce the chalkdust on the teacher's clothes. Chalkholders for white and colored chalk will reduce the chalk layer on the hands. But a convenient facility for washing hands after an hour at the chalkboard is most appreciated.

CHALKBOARDS It cannot be repeated too often that adequate chalkboard is important in a mathematics classroom. A discussion of the mathematics classroom should not omit chalkboards, even though these are to be discussed in detail in Part IV. In a college mathematics class the chalkboard should cover the entire front wall, and there should be additional chalkboard space accessible for student use on the side or back walls. For classrooms having more than five rows of seats it is desirable that all or at least part of the front chalkboard should be arranged on vertically sliding panels so that the lecturer's writing is always up at about shoulder height and can be seen easily in the back of the room. If the front chalkboard is fixed to the wall, it is advisable to have a map rail above the chalkboard from which graphs or charts or other displays can be hung. If the front chalkboard slides vertically, other provision must be made for hanging objects. If a demonstration slide rule is used in a room, it may be hung from the ceiling midway between the side walls and about 3 feet in front of the chalkboard, using counterweights so that it can be pulled down or pushed up out of the way; the mount should provide for rotation about a horizontal-longitudinal axis (see p. 131).

Although most of the wall space not occupied by windows or door should be covered with chalkboard, it may be appropriate to have a small bulletin board space on the wall near the entrance to the room. It is also advisable to have bulletin board areas outside the classroom for posting seating lists or other information pertaining to classes using the room. A strip of tackboard above a chalkboard could be used for permanent exhibits such as portraits of great mathematicians.

PROJECTION EQUIPMENT If an overhead projector is to be used in a classroom, provision should be made for properly mounting the screen to avoid distortion of the image (see Part IV).

The use of projection equipment and television for mathematics instruction is likely to increase. It is important, therefore, in planning new classrooms that places be provided where projection equipment can be placed and connected electrically if desired, and that conduits for television cables be provided which will enable teachers now or in the future to hook up on closed circuit television if they wish.

OTHER ITEMS Other miscellaneous items to be considered in furnishing a mathematics classroom are coat racks for the students and teacher (unless these are provided outside the room), pencil sharpeners for student use, storage space for equipment that is to be kept in the classroom, and possibly a basin by the chalkboard, as previously mentioned. The economics of carpeting for classroom floors will be discussed in the section on the high school classroom (p. 132). Suffice it to say here that there are economies in the use of carpeting which may partially or even wholly offset its higher initial cost.[45]

It needs to be emphasized that good acoustics and good lighting are essential in any classroom, even though large lecture rooms may suffer more from acoustical deficiencies than smaller ones. It avails little for a lecturer to prepare and deliver a fine talk, or to write elegantly on the chalkboard, if he cannot be heard or seen clearly by the class. Furthermore, a large classroom with good acoustics is better for class discussions than a small one with poor acoustics in which questions from the floor cannot be heard by others in the class. The front chalkboard should be lighted by a long fluorescent strip mounted either in the ceiling or out in front of the top of the chalkboard, so as to give good illumination over the whole surface. For the general lighting in the room it is better to have lights from strips or ceiling areas than from individual point sources. If images are to be projected on a screen in a classroom, the instructor should be able to control the lighting in such a way that students have adequate light for note-taking but can still see a contrasting image on the screen.

When all the functional requirements of a mathematics classroom have been spelled out and checked off, there still remains something more subtle and less easily defined that needs attention. The classroom should be a pleasant place in which to work. Color should be used effectively to produce a sense of well-being. Variety is achieved by using different color combinations in different classrooms. Many mathematicians would prefer to have their chalkboards gray-black, but they would welcome color in the trim, the walls, and the chairs.

Rooms for desk calculators

The typical mathematics classroom is not well suited to instruction in computation with desk calculators, since persons using these machines need much more table space than is provided by a tablet armchair or even by a 1-foot-wide writing ledge. Tables 24 to 30 inches wide provide adequate space both for the machine and for notes and papers (Fig. 25), but such tables should be sturdily built to minimize vibration. Because of their greater speed and efficiency, electrically operated desk calculators are preferable for computation to the less expensive hand-operated type on which the operator turns a crank to add, subtract, multiply, or divide. (The latter may have some advantages in teaching school children the fundamentals of our decimal system of numeration.) In planning a room for desk calculators it is important to provide for electrical outlets for connecting electrical desk calculators even at institutions where the hand-operated type may be currently in use. These outlets may be provided at 3- or 4-foot intervals along the walls if machines are to be used on ledges or tables along the walls; but there should also be outlets at suitable intervals along the floor of the room to service each of the tables that are not next to the walls. These tables themselves should be provided with a number of outlets, one for each calculator, connected to an outlet near or through a table leg.

A room equipped with desk calculators is commonly called a "statistical laboratory," since practical work in statistics involves a substantial amount of this type of calculation. A statistical laboratory may serve two related purposes. It may be a room in which a class of 20 to 35 students are given formal instruction in the use of desk calculators, and it may also be a room in which students come at most hours of the day to

FIGURE 25 *Statistical laboratory, University of Michigan*

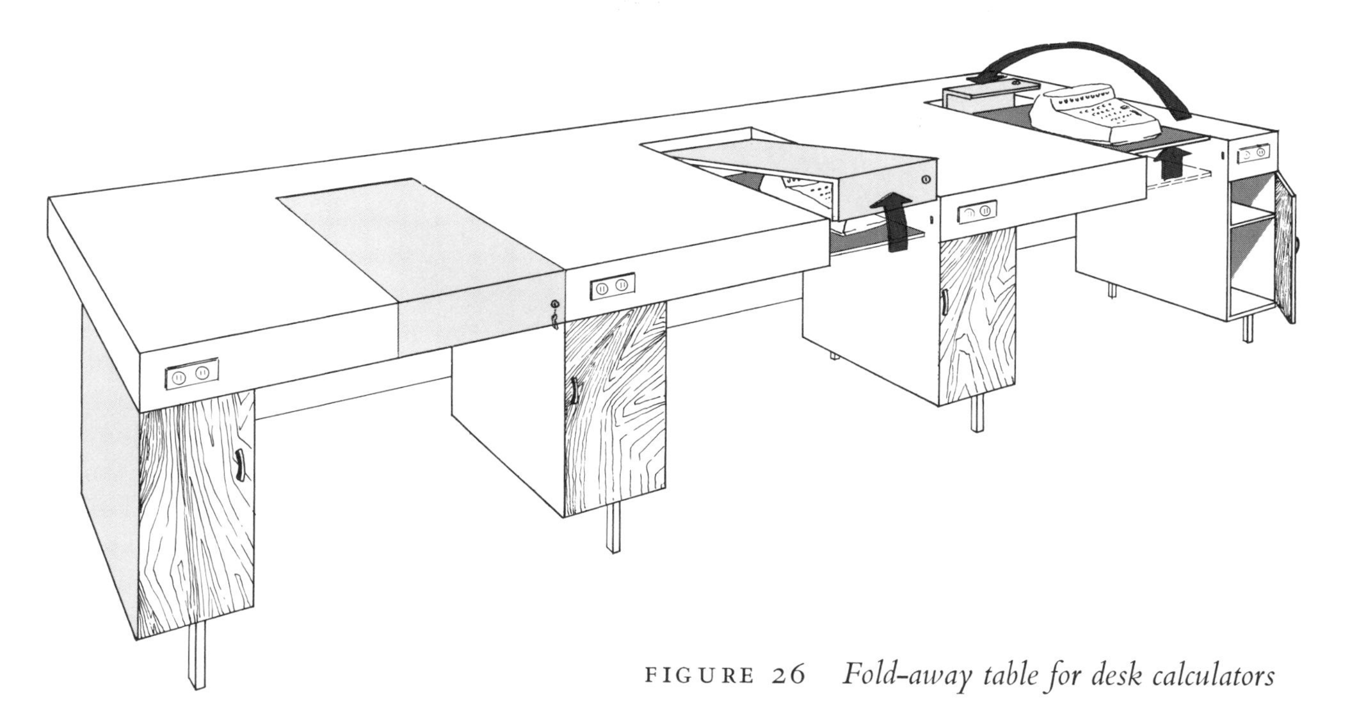

FIGURE 26 *Fold-away table for desk calculators*

work on problems. For the purposes of instruction there should be chalkboard at the front of the room and at least as many calculators as there are students in the class. For maximum usefulness it is important that the room be open to students for many hours a week and that during a number of these hours someone be available to give individual instruction and assistance. It may be necessary to provide supervision of the machines at some institutions to prevent costly damage or theft. Ideally, a laboratory supervisor should have an office adjacent to the statistical laboratory (see Figs. 7b, 8a, 10b) and separated from the laboratory by a glass partition so that he may observe the laboratory while doing his own work. The department may wish to provide cupboards in the statistical laboratory in which the machines could be stored when not in use. Possibly tables for desk calculators could be constructed with a built-in arrangement for storing the calculators similar to the arrangement for storing a typewriter in a secretarial desk (Fig. 26).

Certainly every statistics department and every combined mathematics and statistics department in a large university should have at least one statistical laboratory close to its own offices for the use of staff and students. In a small college it may be possible to have a few desk calculators available to students in a room adjacent to the departmental headquarters; this room could be controlled at all hours by the departmental secretary and attended during special office hours by an instructor or assistant who could help students with their work. At the other extreme, a large university with an active program in statistics may have need for two or three statistical laboratories of which one might be attached to the computing center, another attached to the statistics department, and a third strategically located near other departments whose work involves extensive use of desk calculators.

Acoustical considerations are even more important in a statistics laboratory than in an ordinary classroom. To reduce the noise involved when many people are working simultaneously on the machines, it is advisable to have acoustically treated ceilings and upper wall surfaces and a carpet on the floor.

Seminar rooms

A seminar room for mathematics usually seats 10 to 25 persons in such a way as to encourage discussion and interaction among members of the class. A room of this kind should be provided with adequate chalkboard on at least two walls, since most mathematical ideas are more easily presented visually than by the spoken word. The seating arrangement in this room may be informal, so that each student can see most of the others. In a department with an active graduate program, faculty members and graduate students may organize seminars and have regular weekly meetings on any mathematical topic of mutual interest. Seminar rooms provide a convenient place in which an instructor can meet groups of his students who come for an office hour to ask questions about his course. Flexibility in the size of groups that may be met in a seminar room is achieved if two such rooms are placed adjacent to each other with a movable, soundproof partition between them which may be opened to combine the two rooms into a larger one (Fig. 53). Such partitions are discussed later in this chapter (p. 71). As in the classroom, the seminar room should have good chalkboard, good acoustics, good lighting, and a pleasant atmosphere.

Spaces for individual study

Spaces for individual study are of several types. They include offices for teaching assistants and research assistants. They also include the student reading room and library, where students may do individual work although they are seated in a large room with others. These spaces are in common use today and will be discussed later. Another type of individual study space rarely seen today, but probably soon to be found on college campuses, is space especially adapted to the use of teaching machines or programed instruction (see p. 149).

Materials for programed instruction range in complexity from spiral notebooks, in which students read and answer a succession of graded questions enabling them to progress by small steps through a course of study, to complicated electrical machines that present questions to students by voice and film. The latter may provide elaborate variations of the program that depend on the students' response, offering extensive drill for the slow student and permitting the quick learner to proceed rapidly through the course. It is not expected now that programed instruction will replace classroom teaching for the majority of students, but rather that it will serve as a valuable supplement to classroom teaching. As college mathematics enrollments steadily increase, many college departments are refusing to offer instruction to remove deficiencies in high school algebra, geometry, and trigonometry. Students with deficiencies in these subjects are either not admitted to college or are admitted but required to make up the deficiencies on their own. Programed instruction might enable deficient students to overcome their deficiencies without faculty instruction. Those who miss standard freshman work because of illness may be assisted by programed instruction to fill in the gaps by independent study. Programed instruction may likewise make it easier for a good student who wishes to study a calculus course independently to answer appropriate questions on the material and yet proceed at his own fast learning pace without being held back by a class. Programed instruction might be used to teach the elements of the slide rule to students who feel the need of such instruction for their work in other science departments. Whether programed instruction will be widely used as a supplement to classroom teaching in mathematics remains to be seen, but those who plan a new facility should be aware of its possibilities and provide spaces which could be converted to use for programed instruction, if desired.

Programed instruction by books requires a large amount of storage space and a quiet study area where a student may read, write, and concentrate on his work, but programed instruction by machine may require a more elaborate setup, possibly similar to the laboratories used quite commonly for language instruction. Some thought is being given to an arrangement whereby large groups of students can simultaneously study a block of material, each at his own pace, with a high speed digital computer serving to program a succession of frames that each student uses in a sequence prescribed by his answers. Such a laboratory must be equipped with adequate electrical outlets and possibly cables connecting it to the campus computer, as well as the appropriate number of acoustically private booths.

Flexible partitioning

Flexibility, in the sense of adaptability, is desirable in the sizes and shapes of certain learning spaces, both to permit multiple use and changing use of the space, and to provide for uses that may not clearly be foreseen in the original planning. Long-range flexibility may be needed to allow for the expansion of certain areas, such as the library or computing center; short-range flexibility may be needed to permit two seminar rooms, each used for 15 students during one hour, to be combined into a room for 25 or 30 in the next hour. If a large lecture room is to be used on Monday, Tuesday, and Friday for a mathematics class of 150 students, and if this class is to be split into six small sections of 25 students with three sections meeting Wednesday and three on Thursday at the same hour, space for these sections could be provided in the lecture room itself, were it easily divided into three rooms suitable for such small classes (Fig. 21). Such flexibility presupposes the availability of movable partitions that give sufficient visual and acoustical separation between certain learning spaces.

There are at least four degrees of flexibility in partitions between rooms.[19] A load-bearing partition is completely inflexible and cannot be removed without danger to the building. A non-load-bearing partition, even if made in permanent form of masonry, can be torn out in a few hours when the building is remodeled. A higher degree of flexibility is provided by partitions that can be removed without being destroyed. One type consists of panels that can be set tightly between floor and ceiling and pneumatically sealed by an inflatable rubber strip at the top or bottom. Such partitions can be moved in a fairly short time to rearrange the spaces that they bound. Finally, the most flexible type of partition is one that can be opened or closed on a moment's notice without special tools, so that spaces can be combined or separated by the teacher between classes or even within a class period.

Walls of the last two degrees of flexibility are said to be operable.[19,64] They are manufactured by a number of companies and are being considerably improved in acoustical quality. One of the major requirements of an operable wall is that it effectively reduce sound transmission between the spaces it separates. This reduction in sound is measured in decibels of sound transmission loss. On this scale a 20-decibel loss represents a reduction of sound by a factor of 10 in amplitude, or by a factor of 100 in energy transmission.

A word about the decibel scale may be appropriate at this point. In measuring sound intensities on the decibel scale, the arbitrary zero point is taken as an energy of 10^{-16} watts/cm^2 or 0.002 dynes/cm^2.[67] A 30-decibel level represents an energy 1,000 times as great as this. The threshold of hearing varies with frequency (and with the indi-

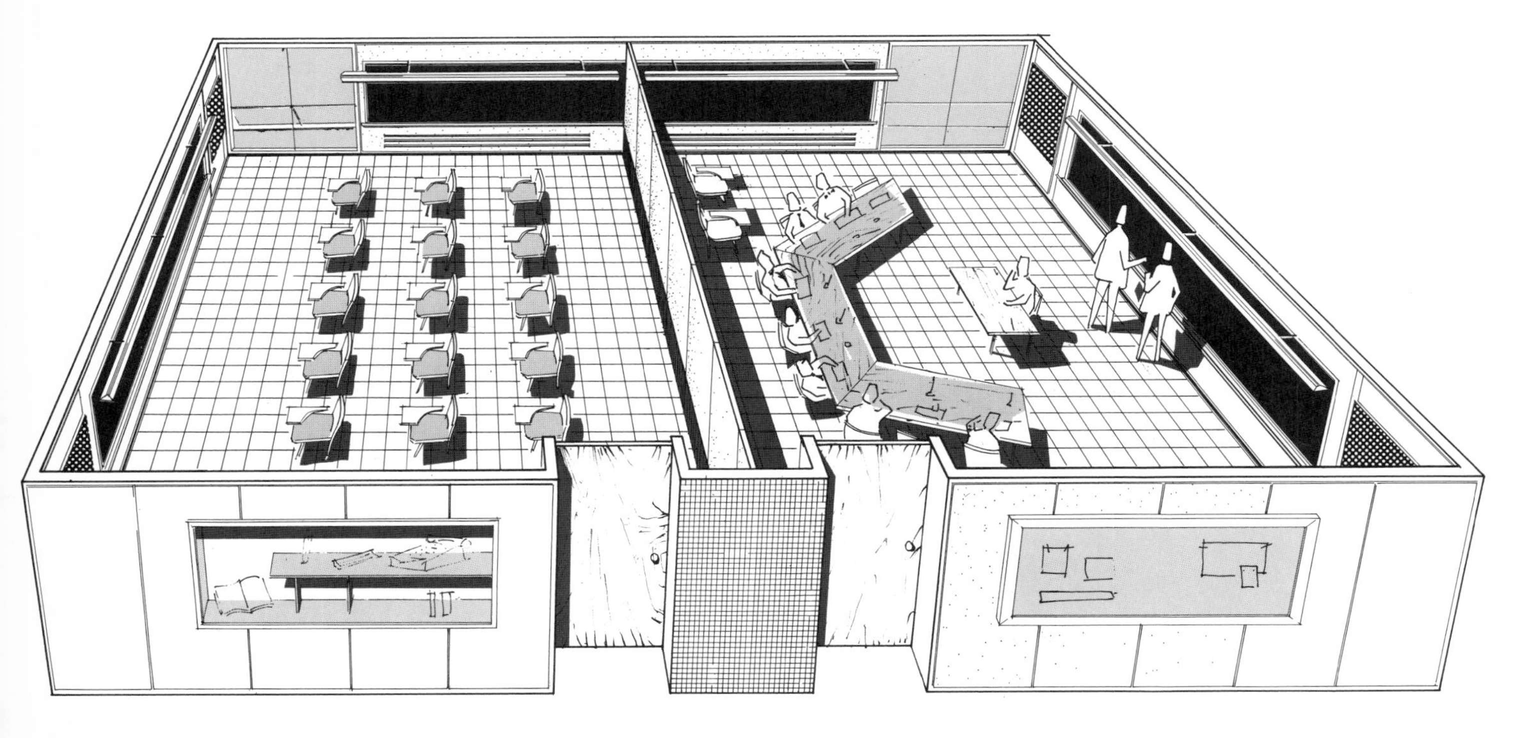

FIGURE 27 *Divisible classroom*

vidual) and has a minimum of nearly 0 decibels in the soprano frequency range. The threshold is louder than this at lower and higher frequencies. Tolerable noise levels may be 15 to 20 decibels in a classroom or 30 in an auditorium. A level of 60 decibels is typical of ordinary conversation. An unpleasant level of 80 decibels is found in the New York subway. The threshold of pain occurs between 110 and 120 decibels. An important acoustical property of a room is its reverberation time. This is the time required for an emitted sound to be reduced by 60 decibels, so that its energy is reduced by a factor of one million, or its amplitude by a factor of one thousand. Optimum reverberation time for speech is about 1.5 seconds, for music about 2.3 seconds.[67]

A typical sound transmission loss for a commercial operable wall might be in the range of 30–35 decibels.[18] Some of the more expensive varieties achieve a 40–45 db S.T.L. Prices for operable walls may vary from $3 to $30 per square foot.[45] To insure acoustic privacy it is important that flexible partitions be fitted tightly against the ceiling, floor, and walls, and that cracks be avoided where two panels come together. A small aperture may transmit as much sound as a square foot of an operable wall.

The amount of sound reduction necessary between two rooms depends on the noise level present in these areas. If the sound passing through the wall is below the background-noise level, it is tolerable; otherwise it is distracting. Since sound transmission between rooms is possible not only through the walls but through the ventilation and air conditioning ducts, these ducts should be treated in certain cases to reduce sound transmission.

Although good operable partitions are not cheap, they may be economical if they permit one space to serve two or more purposes and thereby produce savings in the total space requirement for a building that more than offset the cost of the partition. The important thing is that the partitions should be effective enough as insulators to assure the acoustic privacy that is needed in the areas under consideration. Teachers, who have had unpleasant experiences with poor acoustic insulation, are convinced that no flexible or operable wall can be satisfactory. Yet, recent research has produced operable partitions with sufficiently high sound transmission loss that they can serve effectively to separate two mathematics classrooms and avoid mutual interference.

A room may be divided by a pair of flexible partitions that are pulled out from opposite walls to meet in the middle (Fig. 3), or by a single partition pulled from the back wall to a groove between panels of chalkboard on the front wall (Fig. 27). The latter arrangement has advantages for the teaching of mathematics.

---

5 STUDY AND RESEARCH AREAS

Activities in a mathematics professor's office

The office of a mathematician or statistician must serve a variety of purposes, and decisions regarding the size and arrangement of faculty offices should be made with these functions in view. The office serves as a meeting place where students and colleagues may come for individual or small group conferences with the professor. The office also serves as a private retreat where the professor may prepare for his classes, grade papers, study, or carry on private research. Similar considerations apply to the office of a research mathematician in industry (Fig. 2).

To serve as a meeting place to discuss mathematics, a mathematician's office should be large enough to accommodate both himself and his visitors and should be equipped with that all-important communications device for mathematics—the chalkboard (Figs. 28, 29). Since it is difficult for two office mates to hold simultaneous conferences with different groups in the same room, or for one to study while the other is talking to a group of students, private offices for staff members should be provided whenever possible.

As a center for his research activities, the chief requirements for a mathematician's office are privacy in comfortable surroundings, adequate shelving for books and journals, filing space for papers and reprints of research articles, a chalkboard, and proximity to a mathematical library. Typically, a mathematician must prepare for his research by 1) *reading* in the library, 2) *hearing* lectures and talks by other mathematicians, 3) *discussing* mathematics with colleagues, usually with the aid of a chalkboard, and 4) *thinking* for extended periods of time about his problems. Often the result he finally publishes is not the one he was originally seeking but some by-product seen in a moment of inspiration. After the preparation, stimulation, and inspiration comes a period of elaboration in which ideas are developed, checked in the literature to see if similar results have been published, and polished into publishable form with secretarial help.

Location of offices for faculty and secretaries

The placement of faculty offices relative to classrooms is usually a compromise between two conflicting desires. On the one hand, the professor would like convenient access to his office before class and between classes, so that he may leave his coat in his office before class, pick up notes or paper or demonstration material for class use, and return his things to his office when leaving class for other appointments. On the other hand, particularly in large universities, the professor would like to have his office removed from the congestion and traffic of students in the classroom area. In balancing these two requirements, it seems best to place the faculty offices in the same building, either on a different floor or in a different wing from the main classroom area.

For research purposes a mathematician's office should be quiet and easily accessible to a mathematics library. A mathematician's time in research must be divided between reading for background information on the subject, thinking about problems which interest him, and checking theories which he may discover, both to see whether they are in the literature and to compare them with the ideas of others. After working in his office for an extended period without interruption, the researcher may suddenly need to look up a reference or check an idea in the library. Such activity may be stifled if the library materials are not readily available.

SECRETARIAL ASSISTANCE The productivity of a mathematics faculty can be significantly increased by providing sufficient secretarial help. Time spent by faculty members in typing class notes or research manuscripts and doing similar clerical work that could be done better and quicker by a competent typist or secretary is time taken away from their research and their students. In a period when mathematicians are in short supply, it is es-

FIGURE 28 *Room 115, Fuld Hall, formerly Albert Einstein's office at the Institute for Advanced Study, Princeton, N*

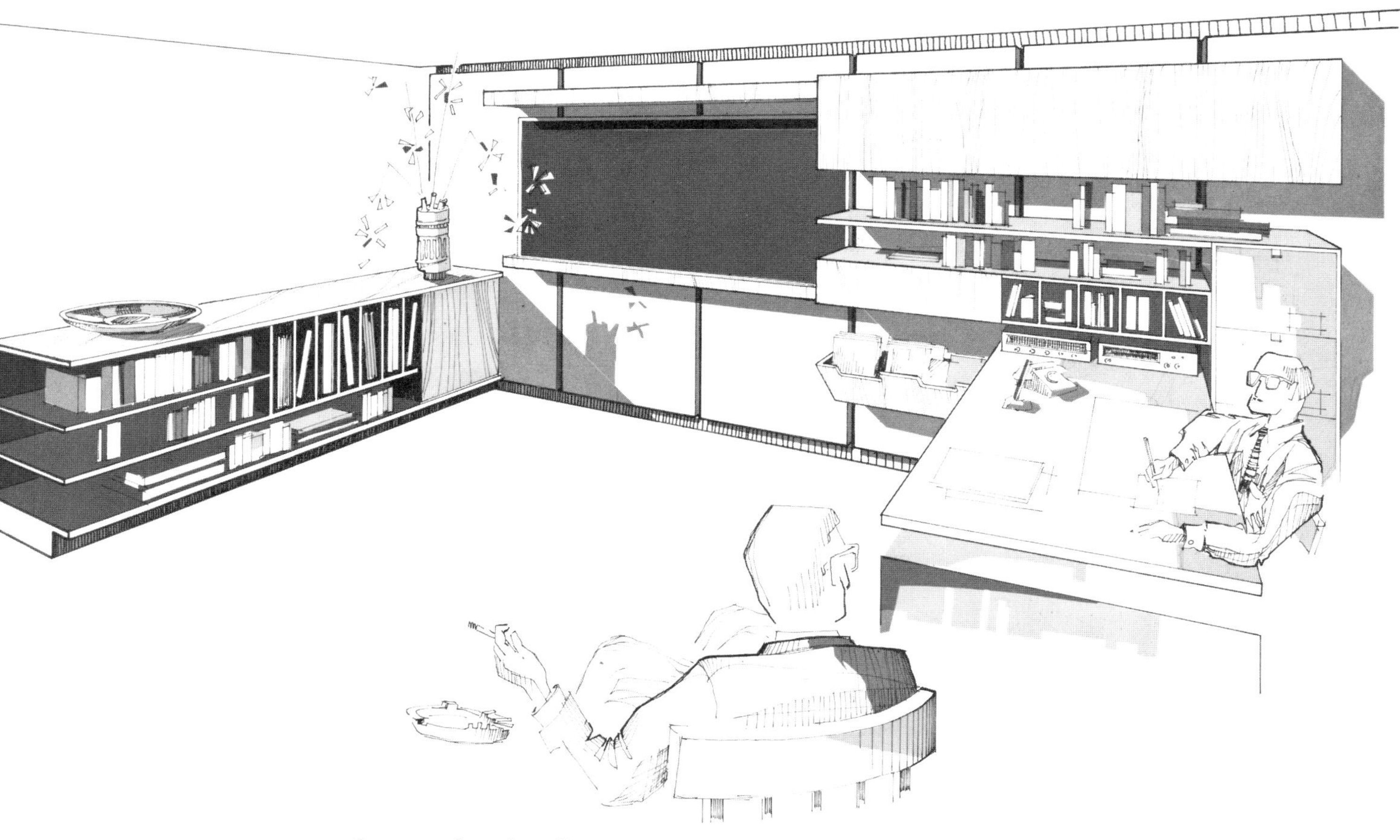

FIGURE 29 *Design for a professor's office*

pecially important to conserve their energies for teaching and scholarly activities. A modest start in this direction would be to have at least one secretary or typist provided for every eight faculty members to assist them in clerical work connected with teaching and research, in addition to the secretarial staff that assists in department administration. Some professors, who are active in research, editorial work, or local and national committee work in addition to their teaching, are justified in requesting the assistance of a half-time or full-time secretary. Offices for these faculty secretaries must be supplied and might be distributed among the faculty offices or concentrated in the departmental headquarters. While two secretaries in an office or three or four in adjacent offices can share specialized skills (taking dictation, technical typing, operating duplicating machines, etc.) and can better maintain service during vacation periods, too large an administrative staff in one area may be inefficient for a large department. Moreover, the involvement of some mathematicians in editorial, consulting, and committee work at a local and national level has now reached a point where the services of a receptionist-secretary to monitor visitors and telephone calls may be fully justified on an individual basis.

Size and equipment of faculty offices

One of the important questions to be decided in planning a mathematics facility is the size of the offices. The answer cannot be categorical, since it depends on the budget and on the use to which faculty members put their offices. The project questionnaire indicated that the median size of private offices for the mathematics or statistics faculty among the 300 institutions reporting was between 140 and 150 square feet. Although more than half of the department chairmen answering the questionnaire seemed to be satisfied with whatever size offices their departments had, a substantial number felt that private offices of less than 132 square feet were too crowded. In Germany, the recognized standard size for a mathematics professor's office is 25 square meters (about 270 square feet), and those of lesser rank usually have offices about two-thirds that size.

Because of the variability in the use of offices, it would seem desirable to plan a mathematics facility with private offices of about three sizes. Smaller offices between 120 and 144 square feet might be suitable for younger staff members, who have neither a large personal library nor responsibilities that require holding group meetings in their offices. Private offices between 180 and 216 square feet, if suitably designed, should be adequate for most staff members. However, even this size may be inadequate for a few individuals whose responsibilities include frequent group meetings in their offices. For example, a statistics professor serving as consultant to many departments in the university may have to include in his office voluminous files for the projects on which he is working, and adequate space for a conference table to seat six or more persons. The department head may need a larger office unless he has ready access to a conference room in which he can hold group meetings. In any case, his office should be large enough to hold his own personal library and files and to confer with groups of three or four people.

Initial plans for a new mathematics facility might well include a number of larger private offices which could if necessary accommodate two people as the staff grows.[20] Staff members or secretaries who share an office should have at least 80 to 100 square feet per person. Somewhat more would be desirable. Offices for more than two regular staff members or secretaries are to be avoided, since overcrowding makes for inefficient work in the office.

In designing one of the smaller private mathematics offices (less than 150 square feet), it is important to place the doors so that there are ample wall spaces for a panel of chalkboard and for a minimum of four 6-foot shelves or six 4-foot shelves for books and journals. Some teachers like to have their desks next to the wall, and this has advantages for connecting telephone equipment. The telephone outlet should be near a convenient position for the person seated at the desk. Unfortunately, it is only too commonly found under the chalkboard. Built-in bookshelves occupy less floor space than portable bookcases and are desirable if properly placed. Sliding glass panels in front of such shelving will keep out much of the dust, but some teachers prefer to have open shelves.

EQUIPMENT Each faculty member should have at least one four-drawer letter file in his office, and many will need two or more. These files require a suitable wall space. A wardrobe or coat rack also requires wall space. A possible arrangement that includes files, wardrobe, and bookcases in a compact arrangement on one wall is as follows. A wall space 10 to 12 feet long and 30 inches deep between two offices is built to contain two wardrobe closets up to a height of 7 feet, and two recessed areas 30 inches wide and 5 feet high, each large enough to contain two four-drawer letter files, and arranged so that one wardrobe and one pair of files opens into each office. Above the files, built-in bookcases 12 to 15 inches deep in each office are separated by a common wall up to ceiling height. Enclosed storage space is likewise provided above the wardrobes. Each closet might contain a 1-foot rod halfway back and parallel to the wall for hanging coats, and shelving space about 18 to 24 inches wide for storage of books, notes, and other materials. A mirror on the door of such a closet would be desirable for all teachers, and essential for women teachers. Ample space for chalkboards, as well as space for additional bookcases, could be reserved on the opposite wall of the office.

A successful idea for a mathematics office recently adopted in the remodeling of facilities at the University of Washington is the following. In these offices upright standards are installed on three walls, spaced for a common 4-foot module. Windows occupy the fourth wall. Shelving and chalkboards are provided which can be attached to these standards in 4-foot widths. A typical office includes 8 feet of chalkboards and 8 feet of shelving six tiers high, but the components are adjustable and interchangeable. A similar idea is shown in Figure 30.

The return of papers to a professor by his paper grader is facilitated if the door to his office contains a slot through which papers can be dropped into a box fastened to the door on the inside. This box should be deep enough to prevent pilfering. A slot about 1½ inches deep and 12 inches long should permit papers to be dropped in easily without permitting people to reach in from the outside. An alternative is to provide for the return of papers in the department mail room (see p. 159).

The lighting arrangements for two areas of the office are of particular importance; namely, the area over the desk and the area over the chalkboard. Long, fluorescent lights are preferable to point sources for light illumination. It is important that a faculty office be a quiet place in which to work and one which permits privacy for conferences or telephone conversations. This is particularly important for the chairman, who may often discuss salaries and personalities with the Dean or others. Adequate acoustical insulation is important. Carpeting on the floor of an office is not only

FIGURE 30 *Design for a professor's office showing modular-wall construction*

attractive but utilitarian. It is a good insulator for both sound and heat and is less expensive to clean and maintain than asphalt tile. Over the 10-year life of a carpet, the savings in maintenance may come close to the initial cost differential[45] (see p. 83).

As mentioned before, there is need for offices of various sizes. Those larger than the minimum size should provide additional space for bookshelves, files, and storage space protected from dust. There should also be room for a small conference table with chairs for three or four people. Two items found as standard equipment in professors' offices in mathematical institutes in Germany are a wash basin near the chalkboard and a sofa or easy chair. If a comfortable easy chair or sofa is an aid to stimulating creative thought, it is not really a luxury. In fact, a mathematician's most important work—thinking creatively—may be done best in a posture that suggests inactivity to those who work primarily with their hands.

Conference rooms and contract research spaces

A conference room is a useful facility for teaching, research, and administration. A large department should have at least one conference room or seminar room seating 15 to 20 persons associated with each group of staff offices, in addition to a conference room of suitable size near the administrative headquarters. The latter might be used for oral examinations, departmental committee meetings, and any other meetings of more than four but less than 25 persons that involve the department head or his assistants.

Conference or seminar rooms (equipped with ample chalkboards) in the faculty office areas might serve one or more of the following needs: 1) faculty members need a convenient place to hold conferences with groups of more than two or three students who may come in together for a question and answer session before a test; 2) small groups of faculty and students may wish to meet together for regularly scheduled seminars that are arranged informally without credit; and 3) if several faculty members and graduate students are cooperating on a research contract, they may need a place larger than a private office where they can exchange ideas.

Seating in a mathematics conference room may be around a large table or it may be in movable tablet armchairs arranged in a semicircle so that those present can see one another as well as the chalkboard that covers one wall. A flexible arrangement is to provide trapezoidal tables that can be assembled into a variety of shapes for smaller or larger groups (Fig. 53). In some small colleges where the mathematics department does not have its own library, the departmental conference room might be the repository for selected journals and books that would be available to staff members and advanced students for reference and browsing.

Occasionally, research contracts on a university campus are of such magnitude that they require the full-time assistance of one or more typists and secretaries to type the reports and keep the books. Some contracts also require security storage. If so, appropriate space and facilities must be available.

Offices for graduate assistants

Space allocated to graduate assistants is usually a compromise between what is desirable and what is economically feasible. Most graduate students will do better work if they have some privacy than if they have to share an office with four to a dozen others. Single or double offices for all graduate students would be the ideal. The best-housed departments with large numbers of graduate assistants provide offices of between 160 and 240 square feet, to be shared by two assistants. Yet, even a desk in a crowded office is better than no desk at all. When budget limitations severely restrict the amount of space available to graduate students, certain compromise arrangements will at least give the teaching assistant a quiet place where he can study and where he can meet his students. One arrangement is to provide separate spaces for study and talk. Talking is done in a common conference room of perhaps 400 square feet having at least two walls lined with chalkboards and provided with enough chairs and tables so that several teaching assistants can see their students in small groups simultaneously. Adjacent to the conference room is a group study office kept quiet for study purposes, in which each graduate assistant has a private desk, bookshelves, and file, possibly in a private cubbyhole like a library carrel, separated by glass partitions from the study areas of the other students. Acoustic privacy and good lighting are important considerations for such study areas. An arrangement of space for graduate assistants at the University of Oklahoma is described in a later section as a possibility for office space for high school teachers (p. 126).

Student reading room

Students in colleges and universities with high standards have more academic work to do outside of class than inside class. Many also have to spend from four to 20 hours a week outside of class on income-producing jobs. It is important, therefore, that they make the best use of their free periods between classes. To accomplish this they should have a place to study that is not more than five minutes removed from the classroom. If only the library reading room is available, this room must serve not only library users, but all those doing homework not involving the use of library materials. To avoid this overcrowding and to save the library reading room for library users, it is highly fitting to provide a study room in each building, where students may work during a free period. The room should be easily accessible to the classroom area and should be provided with a sufficient number of tables and chairs. If college policy permits smoking in certain university rooms but not others, it might be helpful to divide the students' study area by a flexible partition into two areas, one for smokers and one for nonsmokers. In addition to having adequate seating and well lighted writing surfaces, the students' study area should be treated either by acoustic tile or carpets to insure a quiet place in which to work. Desirable equipment should include coat racks, a drinking fountain, and a pencil sharpener.

---

6 DEPARTMENTAL LIBRARIES

The importance of an accessible mathematics library

A mathematics library, adequate in coverage of books and research journals, and conveniently located near the offices of the senior mathematics staff, is a primary requisite of any mathematics department. It is an absolute necessity, if a department is to compete successfully in recruiting research mathematicians. It is as essential to the research worker in mathematics as the experimental room or laboratory is to the experimental physicist or chemist. A departmental library for mathematics in a large university, or one shared with other related science departments in a medium-sized college, is sometimes difficult to obtain because of cost. But if the main library is not close to the mathematics department (so that a book or journal can be obtained in less than five minutes), the cost of a separate library is justified as the price one has to pay for having an adequately housed mathematics department.

To appreciate the importance to a mathematician of an easily accessible and sufficiently large collection of mathematical books and journals, it is necessary to consider how a mathematician does research. Although no two individuals are exactly alike, the following pattern may be fairly typical. The seed of an idea may be planted either in a mathematical talk, in a conversation with colleagues, or in reading a mathematical treatise or journal. Sometimes this seed takes root right away and grows into a mathematical idea worth publishing in its own right. Sometimes it lies dormant for a while and is only reactivated by new stimuli resulting from further reading or talking with kindred spirits. But the elaboration of the idea usually involves two essential ingredients: a mathematician must have periods of uninterrupted time to try out and develop his own ideas, and he must supplement this independent study by consulting the works of others. Seldom does a mathematician go to a library to read a book from cover to cover. Usually it is to check one or two references, or to browse in the literature of a certain field to find what has been written on a specialized topic. Often it is vital to be able to check an idea at once. A book collection ten or fifteen minutes away in a central campus library does not meet the important condition of ready accessibility. The cost in time required to look up a reference becomes prohibitive.

Mathematical institutes in the leading universities in Germany, Denmark, and many other countries, are built around the mathematics library as a focal point. The same is true in certain leading mathematical centers in the United States, such as Princeton (Figs. 31, 32) and Chicago (Fig. 33).

FIGURE 31 *Reading room, Fine Hall Mathematics Library, Princeton University*

FIGURE 32 *Stacks, Fine Hall Mathematics Library, Princeton University*

FIGURE 33 *Reading room and stacks, Eckhart Hall Mathematics Library, University of Chicago*

Both Fine Hall at Princeton and Eckhart Hall in Chicago have excellent mathematics libraries close to the mathematics offices. The new mathematics building at Dartmouth has a pleasant mathematics library on the second floor, and the new mathematics building at the University of Wisconsin adjoining the physics building contains a joint physics-mathematics library, using parts of two floors (Fig. 5). The joint library for the departments of Mathematics, Physics, and Statistics at Michigan State University, conveniently located on the second floor of the Physics-Mathematics building (Fig. 34),[52] is a great asset to the research activities of these departments, but it is already becoming so crowded that the older bound journals are shelved on high shelves accessible only by ladder, and some new stacks have usurped space intended for readers. A library for physics and mathematics at Oberlin College (Figs. 35, 36) is in the building shared by these departments.

All but one of the ten top teams in the 1961 national William Lowell Putnam competition in mathematics were from institutions having either a separate library for mathematics or one shared with physics or physical sciences. However, many mathematics departments are not so fortunate and find their research program handicapped by having mathematics books and journals collected so far from the mathematics offices that they are not readily accessible.

A separate mathematics library or one shared with related science departments is still desirable but perhaps not so essential on a small campus where the library and mathematics departments are housed in adjacent buildings. Even in such circumstances, however, a small reading room devoted to mathematics might well be placed close to the faculty offices for the convenience of the

FIGURE 34 *Reading room, Physics-Mathematics Library, Michigan State University*

FIGURE 35 *Reading area, Physics-Mathematics Library, Oberlin College*

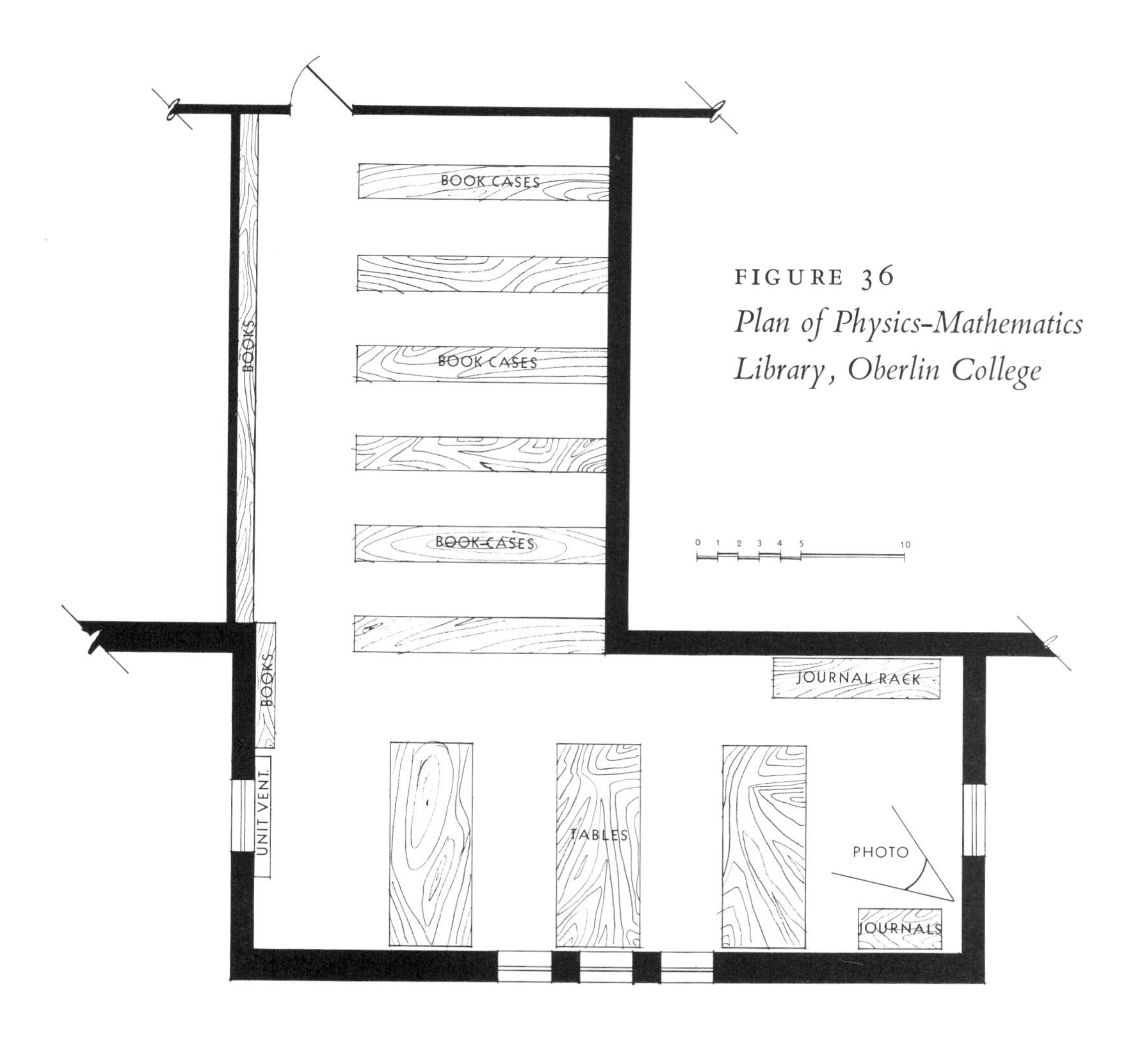

FIGURE 36
Plan of Physics-Mathematics Library, Oberlin College

staff. Possibly, all new issues of journals might be displayed there for a period before being returned to the main library. Duplicates of the more important treatises and of one or two of the leading journals might be maintained there for ready reference. Such a facility would be an invitation to spend that extra ten minutes before class in looking at new journals or brochures; in fertile minds such browsing may plant the seeds of new ideas.

The contents of a mathematics library

The contents of a mathematics library will naturally depend to a certain extent on the size and nature of the institution. In an institution which offers no graduate work in mathematics, there should be a good collection of mathematical books and journals that are stimulating to the undergraduate reader. There should also be books and journals bought principally for the stimulation and enlightenment of the faculty members, who must continue to study and learn throughout their lives.

If two collections of mathematical books and journals are to be maintained on the same campus, the mathematics department should carefully consider and specify, with due regard for the needs of others, which books should be in the department library, which in the main library, and which are needed in both.

A mathematics department offering graduate degrees in mathematics should have a research library. Ideally, such a research library should have available all the current periodicals in which mathematical papers are published, all back volumes of such journals since 1900 or earlier, and all mathematical books of upper division, graduate, or research level. But the prodigious growth in the rate of mathematical publication mentioned on page 5 makes this ideal difficult to achieve. Over 13,700 mathematical articles from 1,000 journals were reviewed by *Mathematical Reviews* in 1962, and the rate of publication continues to increase. Quite a few more than these 13,700 articles were published in 1962, and strenuous efforts have recently been made to reduce the backlog of articles delayed in review.

An indication of the number of mathematics and statistics journals currently being received, the number of bound volumes of books and journals shelved, the number of linear feet of shelving space for these books, and the area in square feet of library floor space (including reading areas and stacks) is given in Table 3 for institutions of various sizes. The figures are derived from data returned in May 1962 in response to a brief postcard-sized questionnaire sent to mathematics departments that had indicated in the earlier project questionnaire that they had either a separate library for mathematics or a branch library shared with other science departments. The responding institutions were classified into three almost equal groups according to their 1960 mathematics enrollments, the "medium-sized" institutions being defined as those for which this mathematics enrollment was between 501 and 1500. Each of the three groups was further split into two types according to whether the library was for mathematics alone or was shared with other science departments. In the case of shared library facilities, the data refer to mathematics and statistics books and to the portion of shelving and library space assigned to these departments. Some incomplete replies and a few that appeared to be inaccurate guesses were discarded. Some extreme figures were questionable, and others were atypical. Therefore, in each of the six groups of institutions considered, the top quarter and bottom quarter of the replies were discarded, and a typical figure was arrived at by considering medians and means of each middle subset, and rounding off results to two significant figures.

Rough as they are, these figures give valuable indications of space required for a typical mathematics library. It is not surprising that large institutions are able to subscribe to more journals, purchase more books, and devote more space to a mathematics library than smaller institutions. Several of the best-equipped institutions subscribe to over 200 mathematical journals and have mathematics collections exceeding 10,000 volumes. But the density of books in the given space and the expected percentage growth are quite comparable in different sized institutions. It will be noted that six volumes per linear foot of shelving and five volumes per square foot of library area is typical for the medium-sized institutions. Conditions appear to be slightly less crowded for small institutions and more crowded for large institutions with shared library facilities. In all but the large shared libraries, a doubling of the number of volumes between 1962 and 1970 is the typical expectation. The planning of new library facilities for mathematics must take this growth factor into account.

Library location and expansion

When all the departments sharing a branch library have their offices in the same building, the library should preferably be in a location easily accessible to students and staff but removed from the noise and congestion of the entrances to large lecture rooms. To avoid such congestion, a second or third floor location may be preferable to the ground floor. Possibly a general study room might be located under or adjacent to the library for use by students who wish to study between classes but are not using the library books. This will relieve the library reading area from unnecessary overcrowding.

The almost explosive growth in the number and size of mathematics publications makes it difficult to predict accurately the amount of space required for the library of the future. The estimates indicated in Table 3 may turn out to be conservative. Stack space with a provision for doubling the current number of books may be inadequate before 1970. Possibly the only feasible way to solve the problem of storage space for mathematical books and articles is to store some of the less used publications on microfilm or magnetic tape. Immense amounts of material can be stored on a single roll of magnetic tape, but the usefulness of such information depends to a large extent on its accessibility. Scholars cannot easily browse in a magnetic tape. Perhaps in the near future computers may provide the answer to information retrieval. But computers alone could not do the job. They would have to be assisted by persons trained in both mathematics and library

TABLE 3 *Typical Data for Mathematics Libraries*

Size of institution (1960 mathematics enrollment)	*Type of library*	*Number of journals (1962)*	*Bound volumes (Mathematics)*		*Shelving (Linear feet)*		*Library area (Square feet)*	
			Actual (1962)	*Expected (1970)*	*Actual (1962)*	*Needed (1970)*	*Actual (1962)*	*Needed (1970)*
Small (500 or less)	Separate	40	2,300	4,700	460	980	560	910
	Shared	20	1,000	2,200	230	370	370	530
Medium (501–1,500)	Separate	100	4,000	8,000	660	1,100	800	1,100
	Shared	90	4,000	7,000	660	1,100	800	1,100
Large (more than 1,500)	Separate	150	7,500	15,000	1,200	2,200	2,000	4,000
	Shared	120	7,000	11,000	800	1,600	1,000	1,800

science who could perform two essential functions: they could codify the information in a new book, possibly under as many headings as there are items in its index, and they could also assist a reader to ask the computer a question that would elicit a complete bibliography as a response. If such developments should take place, it would be important to have suitable conduits in the building for connecting the library to the computer installation. If the library does grow rapidly, it is essential to have space adjacent to the library that can be converted later into library space without undue cost.

Such convertible space might be an office or a classroom. It might be a general study room contiguous to the library on the same floor or possibly directly under the library so that it could be reached from the stack area by a staircase. At first such an area would serve students who wish to study between classes and do not need library materials for a particular assignment. If later the library required the use of this space, the general study room could be relocated. The study room itself should be provided with tables and chairs for written assignments as well as some more comfortable chairs for reading assignments. A student who has classes for three of the four morning periods needs a place where he can be comfortable during the vacant period. If this comfort is provided in an atmosphere conducive to study, the hour will not be wasted.

Reading, study, stack, and reference areas

There is need for three types of reading areas in a mathematics library. One area should provide tables and chairs for a large number of people who may wish to spread out their books and papers and take notes while they read. A second type of reading space should be provided for the person who wants to look up a reference or to browse, and will only use a given book for a few minutes. Adequately lighted, isolated chairs in the stack area might serve this need. Finally, it is desirable to provide some secluded carrels with a well-lighted writing surface and shelving for a few books where a student doing research on a topic can temporarily leave books and papers, possibly in a locker. Such spaces might be assigned to individual students for limited periods at the discretion of the librarian.

Stack areas in a mathematics library should be as accessible as possible to students and staff, with the possible exception of certain rare book collections, which might be kept under lock and key. Open stacks are much more useful as a research tool than closed stacks. Often the research worker does not know which book or journal he should consult but must first browse around to find out what is available. The cost of replacing a moderate number of books that may be stolen or borrowed without being signed for may be less than the cost of personnel to keep close supervision on people leaving and entering the stacks. Exceptions to the policy of open stacks should only be made if experience on a given campus shows the book loss rate with open stacks to be prohibitive.

Reference areas in a mathematics library include not only the card indexes giving titles and authors of books, and a complete list of journals with call numbers, but also a bibliographical center including a complete file of *Mathematical Reviews,* and files of other reviewing journals such as the *Jahrbuch über die Fortschritte der Mathematik,* the *Zentralblatt für Mathematik,* and others. These reviewing journals should be kept as a unit in the library, possibly on one or more tables, in order to facilitate the copying of references.

Current periodicals and exhibits

Current issues of mathematical journals should be displayed on open shelves for easy reference. One very good arrangement observed in the mathe-

FIGURE 37 *Mathematics library, Aarhus Universitet, Denmark*

matics library in Aarhus, Denmark, was a display of current journals on steeply slanted shelves hinged at the top. Pasted on the front of the shelf was a cover of the journal to be stored there, distinguishable from a current cover by the hole in its center. Behind each slanting shelf was a flat shelf for keeping the recent unbound issues of each journal (Fig. 37). In addition to current periodicals it may be desirable to have a special shelf for temporary exhibition of all new books received within the past two weeks. A bulletin board should be provided to keep people informed of recent additions to the library and books on order. A display case might be included either in the library or in the corridors just outside the library for displays of interest to mathematicians and their students, such as models, portraits of famous mathematicians, historical items captioned "Did you know that . . . ," or a problem of the week.

Adjacent conference areas

A useful adjunct to a mathematics library found in a number of universities is a small room equipped with a table, two or three chairs, and a chalkboard. In this room students and faculty using library materials may confer without disturbing other people. At Fine Hall in Princeton there is such a room in each corner of the library. Flexibility in the size of the group to be accommodated could be achieved by having two small rooms adjacent to each other separated by a flexible partition.

Space for the library staff

Suitable space should be provided near the entrance to a mathematics library for the attendant who assists readers in locating books and checking them in and out. Sometimes this person will be a student working part-time, who is responsible for the ordering, cataloguing, and shelving of new books and journals, and for arranging to have periodicals bound at appropriate intervals. The person responsible for the operation of the library should have adequate space in which to work, preferably a private office adjoining the library complex. Room is also needed for storing books and journals that have been received but not catalogued, and for journals in transit to and from the bindery. Such storage space should be located where the materials can be easily brought in and out of the library. Possibly a dumbwaiter might be provided in which library materials could be brought up directly from a service entrance to the building.

Microfilm, magnetic tape, and copying equipment

A complete library service must provide access not only to books, but to microfilm and other media for storing information. The use of microfilm requires suitable spaces for reading and fireproof spaces for storage. It may also require photographic equipment for producing copies of materials stored on film. If use is to be made of material stored on magnetic tape, it may be that such material will be recovered for the reader by means of a high speed printer in response to coded requests. Pages of printed books can already be copied quickly and accurately by commercial devices available to libraries at relatively low rental cost. These devices can make it feasible to issue a copy of a particular scientific article to an interested reader for his own use instead of issuing the complete volume and making it temporarily inaccessible to others.

If such devices are to be used in the library of the future, adequate space must be provided for their use and storage.

Computing center libraries

The general problem of securing adequate communication through written records has taken a somewhat new form in the last decade with the advent of digital computers. Among the aspects that need to be considered are these: much "information" is recorded in a form (on cards, tapes, etc.) that can be used only with the aid of a machine costing many thousands or even millions of dollars; publications of direct and immediate interest for the writing of codes for machines tend to be very quickly obsolete, so that normal delays and costs of conventional library acquisition are intolerable; there is a rapidly growing literature in computer science of interest to those professionally engaged in the field; and the literature of interest to *users* of computers is widely scattered through the books and journals of many professional fields.

That some storage for punched cards and magnetic tapes needs to be provided in the immediate (and controlled) environment of the computer will not be doubted. Strictly speaking, this storage of the day-to-day operating supplies is not a "library" question. However, as soon as acquisition of material from other computing centers is involved, some of the normal problems of storing, finding and lending (or, more often than not, providing a copy) arise. Temporary storage for punched cards or paper or magnetic tape for *users* of the computer is highly desirable since a single warped card may cause a problem not to run. The implications of the almost total nonredundancy of computer-used information (so that every character counts) are difficult for one not acquainted with the field to appreciate. Despite the need for storing punched cards carefully, some centers require users to take their cards back to their own offices as a means of controlling the volume of obsolete material that might otherwise occupy computing center storage space.

The kind of information that needs to flow into a computing center will be made clearer if we consider how the users of a given type of computer have formed special associations. The largest of these currently is SHARE, which distributes to each of its members programs (codes) written by any member and deemed of possible general interest. The foreword to one installation's October 1961 edition of the "Abstracts of SHARE Programs for the IBM-704" contains the following statement:

> Current additions and corrections to these abstracts will be distributed periodically. In each case the additional information completely replaces former additions. Furthermore the book of SHARE ABSTRACTS originally distributed in July, 1959, is made entirely obsolete by this version.
>
> More complete write-ups of these routines may be found in Building 203, Room R102, Extension 2885.
>
> The following procedure for utilizing effectively the vast store of material in the SHARE Library is suggested:
>
> 1. Consult the ABSTRACTS to determine which routines may be appropriate for the desired use.
> 2. Read the corresponding complete write-ups in the SHARE Library.
> 3. Request personal copies of the write-ups of those routines which satisfy your requirements.

To be noted is the fact that corrections are distributed frequently, older versions are made obsolete, and current information is available by telephone. Except for five pages of general information, the entire (remaining) 150 pages in this volume was produced completely automatically from information stored on cards or tape. The volume contains between 1,500 and 2,000 abstracts of programs on which further information is supplied on request. These abstracts may be obtained on microfilm or the actual code may be available for machine use on punched cards. Clearly, any computing center requires for efficient operation that someone be responsible for securing, disseminating, and controlling this type of information.

Proceeding on the spectrum of information from the extreme of direct "machine language" toward the general scholarly literature, we find a considerable volume of pamphlet material originating in universities, government laboratories, and industrial computing centers. Although some of this material is eventually published in the indexed literature, failure to be currently informed of it will result in wastage of machine time through the use of obsolete methods. Also, original work in the field is hardly possible without virtually personal contact with those of similar interests. The material under consideration can be read only by those with some knowledge of computer organization and coding, and it is therefore properly kept in the computing center library.

At the next level are the professional journals concerned with the improvement of techniques for computer use. For example, the Association for Computing Machinery publishes its *Communications* and *Computing Reviews* in the United States. There are equivalent journals in England, and similar ones are now published in many other countries. A professional literature in Computer Science thus already exists and will grow rapidly.

The extent to which the computing center library needs to be associated with the main mathematics collection is hotly debated. Certainly, advanced uses of computers require the precise language of mathematics for their description. The lack of interest of most conventional mathematicians in computing has led some computer scientists to prefer being at a distance from the mathematics department. This attitude overlooks the mutual advantage of casual and informal contacts through partially shared library (and social) facilities. These have two important effects: advancing computer science by interesting mathematicians in the field and informing them of it, and providing a salutary reminder to computer staff of the volume of established and excellent literature relevant to their operations. The basic reason for the association is the existence of a common language, and where this does not exist there is a serious loss of precision and clarity in the literature of computing. Possibly a reasonable compromise, where the mathematics and computer sciences share the same or nearby buildings, is to keep the main permanent literature (bound books, journals, etc.) in the mathematics library with adequate space in the adjacent room for material not formally acquired by the library. Alternatively, a completely separate computer science library may be established with any necessary duplication of materials.

---

7 ADMINISTRATIVE AREAS

Departmental administrative duties

Spaces needed for the administration of a department of mathematics or statistics or a computing center, either in a college or university or in an industrial research laboratory, will depend largely on the types of functions to be performed in these spaces. Obviously the needs of a large university department with a teaching staff of 20 to 100 people are much more extensive than those of a small department of two or three. Line drawings of suggested plans for administrative areas were included in Chapter 3 (Figs. 7a, 8a, 10b); many variations may be required to fill the needs of a particular situation. This section is intended to suggest the activities that may be appropriate for a departmental headquarters, and the spaces they require, rather than to attempt to draw a blueprint of universal validity. Needs of the large department in a college or university are emphasized. From this checklist the features appropriate to a smaller college department or to an industrial mathematics or statistics research laboratory may be selected.

The proper operation and development of the teaching and research functions of a mathematics or statistics department depend heavily upon an efficient and well-staffed departmental administration. Unless the department is very small, this work cannot be discharged solely by a departmental chairman and a single secretary; an administrative staff of suitable size and ability must be provided. The chairman should be a first-rate scholar and teacher who directs major policies but is not burdened with all the details of the departmental operations. In a large department, serving more than 1,500 student enrollments or more than 100 mathematics and statistics majors, there should be an associate chairman. As the department grows, additional faculty members may be needed to share specific administrative problems, such as graduate study, undergraduate majors, teacher education, freshman courses, grant and contract negotiations, preparation of class and teaching schedules, supervision of furniture, equipment, and space assignments, and extension and correspondence courses.

There is more than one reason why it is desirable to delegate administrative duties to several members of a department, including an associate chairman. A chairman who is actively interested in teaching and research in mathematics should have the opportunity to continue as a teacher and scholar and should not be so burdened with administrative details that he withers on the vine. He should have at least a month's vacation each year and should be as eligible for sabbatical leaves as other department members. Neither a vacation

FIGURE 38 *Office for reception and secretaries, Department of Mathematics, Michigan State University*

nor leave for the chairman is possible if no one is available to carry on in his absence, since the administrative load connected with increased summer activities in mathematics is often comparable to that during the academic year.

Not only should the chairman have academic assistants, but he should have adequate secretarial help so that he is not required to spend an inordinate amount of time on routine duties. Time saved from such duties might better be spent in teaching or research, or in activities with national organizations.

Reception areas

The focus of the administrative complex is the reception office, where students and visitors of all kinds first arrive and where telephone calls are initially answered (Figs. 7a, 8a, 10b, 38). Adequate space is needed for one or more receptionists, for the central telephone equipment, and for the storage of materials to be made available to visitors. Seating space should be adequate to care for persons waiting to see the various administrative officials.

Many questions directed to this office can be handled promptly by referring the caller to summaries of departmental information posted on an adjacent bulletin board. Among other items, this board should display the departmental directory, class and teaching schedules, and office hours. It should be restricted to items useful to visitors and should not be cluttered by announcements of special meetings, placement, and the like, which are of interest mainly to faculty and students. Other bulletin boards should be provided in more suitable locations (such as hallways and mailrooms) for such announcements.

Faculty administrative offices

The chairman and his faculty administrative assistants should have their offices connected to the reception office. The chairman's office should be large enough to accommodate his own executive desk, chairs for visitors, a conference table, file cabinets, bookcases, a work table, and space for a dictating machine, desk calculator, and typewriter. On one wall there should be a large chalkboard. In some large departments the chairman, or assistant in charge of scheduling classes, finds it helpful to have a large cork board, chart, or chalkboard on which all current teaching assignments are displayed.

Privacy of interviews and of telephone conversations requires that the walls of the chairman's office be soundproofed. Conservation of the chairman's time and energy makes it desirable to provide for him a private washroom so that he is not required to appear in the hall at a time when he cannot afford to be interrupted by casual contacts with his colleagues. The public entrance to his office should be through the reception area, but he needs a private entrance which can also serve as an exit for certain callers.

Some duties of a chairman, both as an administrator and as a scholar, require that he be free from interruptions and distractions for periods averaging at least an hour or two each day. Such privacy is provided either by an inner office or by an isolated research office where he is not "at home" to the usual telephone calls or visitors, but can be reached only in emergencies.

The chairman's faculty assistants should have their offices conveniently grouped in the administrative area, so that callers enter them from the reception area. Their offices may be typical faculty offices with possibly some additional space for files.

For administrative duties not of an academic character the chairman supervising a large and complex operation also needs highly competent non-faculty assistants. Supervision of the secretarial and clerical services may require an office manager. The increasing complications of budgets and financial reports may require an accountant. A large volume of contractual research may call for a proposal writer and contract negotiator. Private offices for these assistants should be very conveniently located with respect to the chairman's office.

Secretarial offices

It is inefficient and uneconomical for highly trained teachers, research workers, and administrators in any department to spend much of their time typing and doing clerical work which could be done as well or better by a typist or secretary. In the mathematical sciences, where shortages of trained personnel are acute, a lack of adequate secretarial help is an inexcusable waste of trained manpower.

The chairman of a large department should have a private secretary in an adjoining office, and secretarial help is required also by his faculty and administrative assistants. Some members of the faculty have research contracts that provide funds for their own private secretaries. Any such specially assigned secretaries should have office space near the faculty member (or members) whom they serve. The faculty at large will also need the assistance of secretaries or typists for typing manuscripts, tests, and correspondence as well as for handling travel arrangements, registration procedures, mail, and messages. These secretaries and typists may be housed in single or double offices located near the department offices, or they may be given office space near the faculty members they are to serve. Somewhere in the building a private rest room with a cot should be provided for their use. Plans should be made for increased accommodations for the secretarial staff as the department grows.

Supporting facilities

Space should be allocated in the administrative

complex for the following supporting activities:

1 *Distribution of faculty mail* Adequate provision should be made for the distribution of mail to faculty and teaching assistants. A mail room is needed for a large department, but this might be combined with a room equipped with duplicating machines. Individual mail slots for faculty members, filled from the mail room but accessible by combination lock from the outside corridor, will reduce congestion in the mail room. Bulletin boards for faculty notices should be placed near the faculty mail slots.

2 *Distribution of notices, mail, and papers to students* Some departments may wish to have provision for distributing notices to all graduate students whether or not they are teaching assistants. Furthermore, if either graduate or undergraduate students are employed as paper graders, it is desirable to have boxes where they may pick up papers for grading, and provision for returning papers to professors. Mail slots for students should be provided in the departmental headquarters, possibly in a separate mail room, unless they are provided in office doors (see p. 77).

3 *Supplies, storage, and safe.* The faculty should have ready access to needed supplies at all times. Current supplies might be kept in a semipublic area, such as the mailroom, and the main stockpile in a secure storeroom. A safe of approved fireproof type should be available for storage of special cash funds, checks, copies of examinations to be given, and other material which must be kept secure.

4 *Secondary storage* A substantial amount of space should be set aside for storage of temporarily unused furniture, personal effects of faculty on leave, extra reprints of departmental publications, copies of course notes, noncurrent departmental records, and desk copies of textbooks formerly used by the department. Some of this storage might conveniently be provided in narrow closets with five or six long shelves, for faculty use, located near faculty offices (Fig. 10d).

5 *A textbook and reprint collection* should be shelved in the departmental headquarters where it is accessible to the faculty. The textbook collection should include the most recent publishers' samples for possible adoption in courses. The reprint collection should include a complete list of publications of each staff member, together with any reprints which the author may wish to make available for distribution. Shelving should also be provided for the temporary storage of desk copies of textbooks awaiting distribution to the faculty and teaching assistants.

6 *A duplicating room* is required with facilities for ditto, mimeograph, and/or multigraph machines as well as appropriate photocopy or Thermofax equipment. Since the operation of this equipment is often noisy, it must be so located that the noise will not bother others. This will usually require a special room to be used for this purpose only. The room should be large enough to contain the needed equipment and supporting work space; a sink is also required. Storage space is needed since a large department may use over 500,000 sheets of duplicating paper a year if it issues three pages per working week to each of 5,000 students. The duplicating facilities might be in a separate room or, as mentioned above, they might be in a large mailroom, provided, of course, that mail boxes are accessible from the outside to prevent congestion.

7 *Examination room* Room is needed for students taking make-up or out-of-season placement examinations. Not much space is required, but it should offer some degree of freedom from outside noise and distractions to the student and at the same time should allow for proctoring, if this is customary. A possible arrangement would be a 5′ x 5′ cubbyhole with a table and chair, separated by a glass wall from a secretary who could if necessary proctor an examination while continuing her work (Fig. 10b). If this area were to be

fully enclosed for the sake of quiet, it would require special ventilation.

Telephone communication, intercom, and dictaphone

The telephone service for a large department should provide service of the following important types:

Each office for faculty, or for teaching and research assistants, should have a phone on which outgoing calls can be made directly.

Provision should be made for incoming calls either to be channeled through the central departmental headquarters or to be received directly in the individual offices. If the central exchange is used, it requires a buzzer system. There should be a way of notifying a staff member of a call received during a brief absence from his office. Some hotels provide such notification by a red light on the telephone instrument, lit by the central operator.

Provision should also be made for the direct receipt of calls in offices during evenings and week ends. If individual offices are dialed directly, there should be an arrangement, if possible, for automatically transferring the call to department headquarters after a reasonable wait, in order that

FIGURE 39 *Three auditoriums with common preparation room*

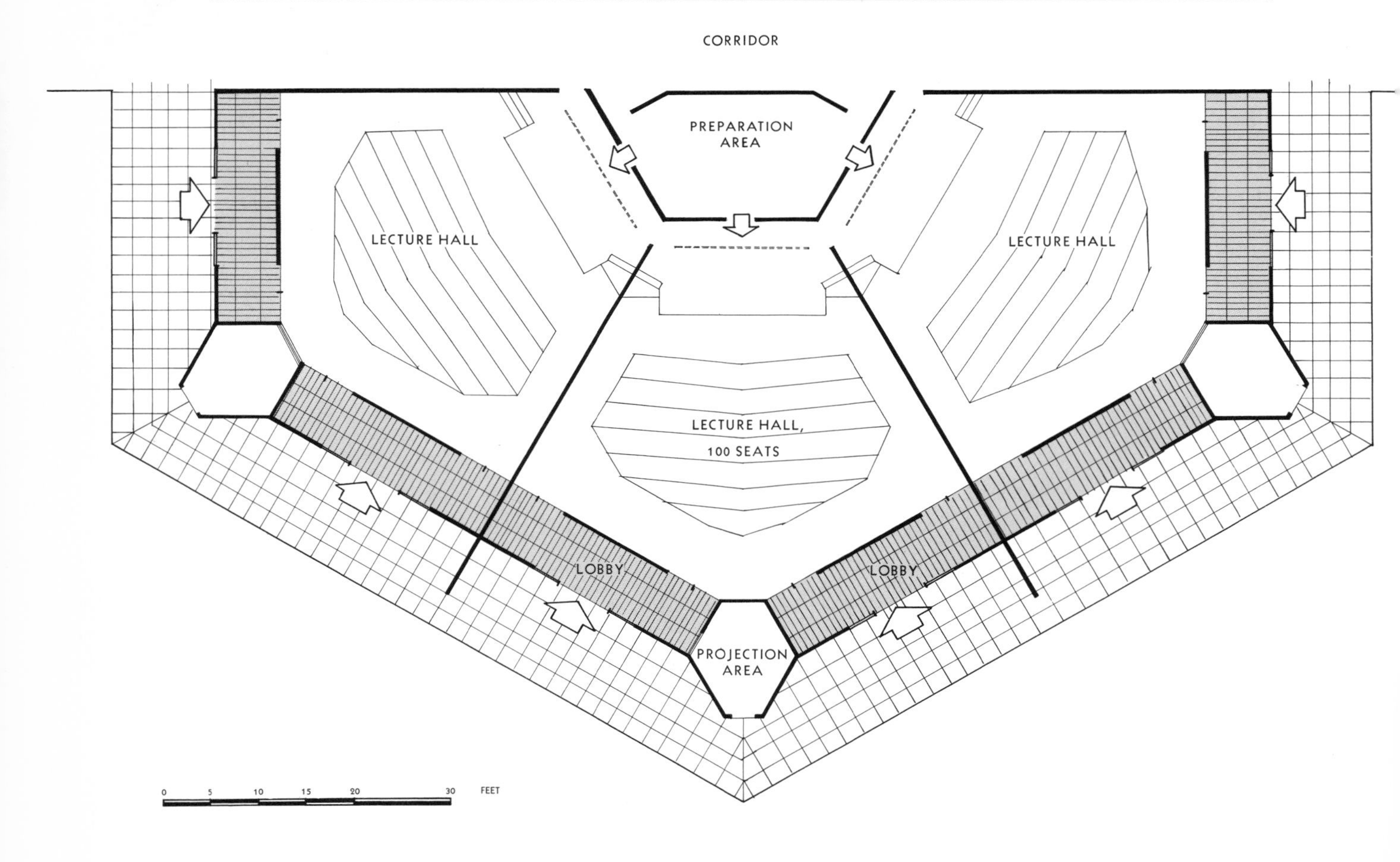

a departmental secretary may take the message.

There should be an intercom system for the personnel in the administrative complex, possibly connected to other offices as well.

A convenience at some institutions is a central dictaphone service reached by dialing its number on the telephone. Staff members may dictate letters, notes, or other material and have them typed and returned from a central office. If such a system is not available, the department head in a medium-sized or a large institution should have a dictaphone in his office.

Visual-aid preparation spaces

With the advent of overhead projectors and other mechanical aids to teaching, room is needed where the faculty—or their aides, secretaries, or assistants—can prepare materials to be used on these machines. A supply of drafting equipment, pencils, special pens and ink, a large-face typewriter, and similar equipment may be required; a sink or wash basin is essential. Unless every class and lecture room has its own overhead projector, storage for department projectors is needed. This space might be in the department headquarters or adjacent to lecture halls (Fig. 39). A machine that can photograph lecture notes directly onto a transparency in a matter of minutes is essential in this room. A collection of textbooks in or near the preparation room would be helpful in the selecting of problems for tests or illustrations. Typewriters for faculty use should be available either in this room or elsewhere in the departmental headquarters.

Conference rooms

Depending on its size, the department will need one or more conference rooms. One of these should be in the administrative complex and might be designed to seat 10 to 20 people around a table. Conference rooms are needed for meetings of department committees, seminars, and oral examinations. They should be equipped with plenty of chalkboard on two or more walls, since the symbolism of mathematics is more easily absorbed by the eye than by the ear. They may also be used as temporary headquarters for visiting speakers, as interview rooms for job placement, or as advisory centers with secretarial help at registration time. For these purposes it is important that each conference room contain a telephone.

---

8 PUBLIC AREAS

Common room or lounge, and kitchenette

Spaces suitable for the exchange of ideas among mathematicians are a necessary complement to a private office and a mathematics library. The department should have, or if necessary share with other departments, a common room or a lounge equipped with comfortable furniture and served by an adjoining kitchenette to provide coffee and refreshments. There can be little doubt that afternoon teas at those universities having such facilities serve as an ideal gathering spot for faculty and students. The communication of ideas in this setting provides an essential part of the educational and research experience of mathematicians (Fig. 40). Either there should be adequate chalkboard on the walls (Fig. 41), or the coffee tables themselves should provide a writing surface where the mathematician may explain his ideas to others. In such a room visiting speakers will be entertained

FIGURE 40 *Mathematics lounge, Eckhart Hall, University of Chicago*

FIGURE 41 *Mathematics lounge, New York University*

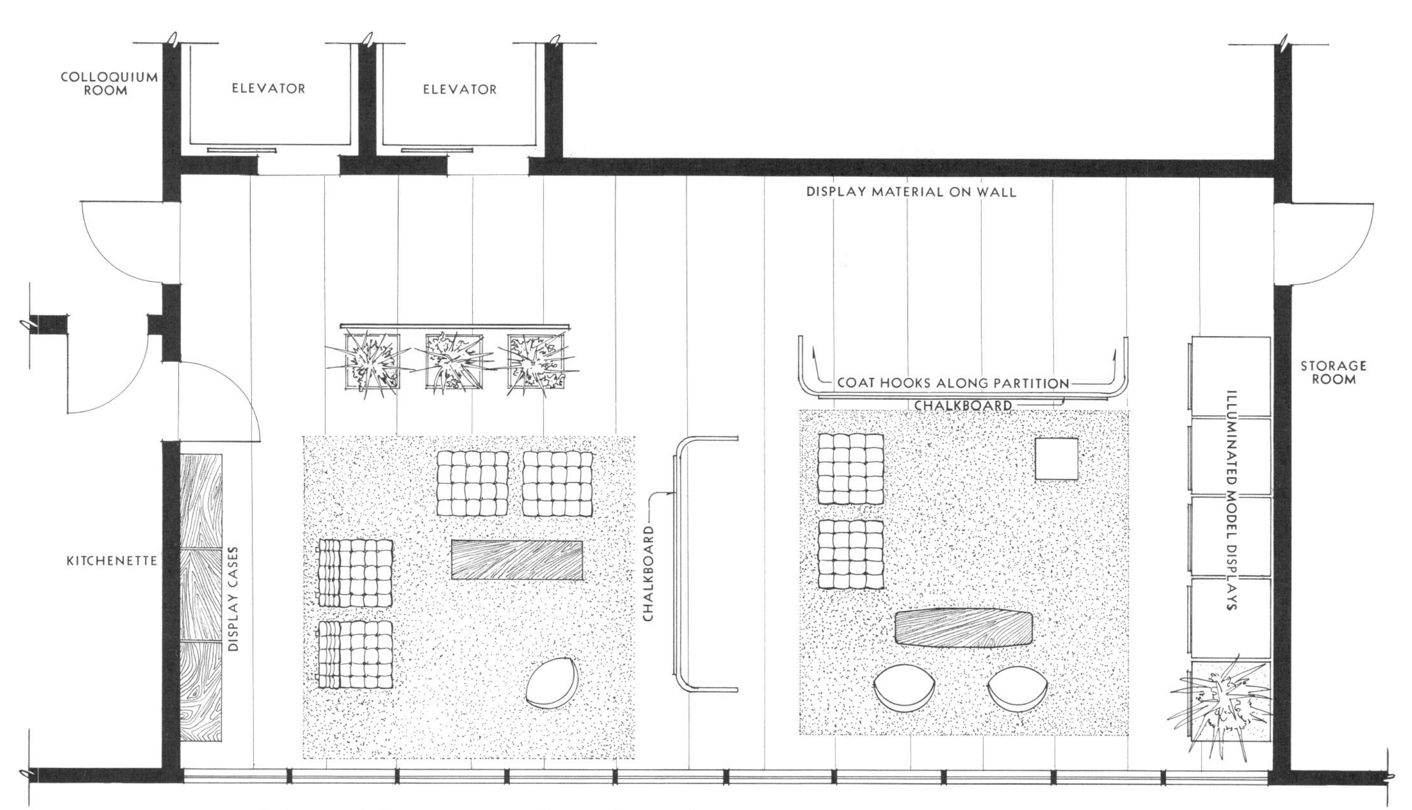

FIGURE 42 *Exhibit and lounge area of top floor plan in Figure 10d*

FIGURE 43 *Kitchenette in mathematics lounge, Dartmouth College*

just before or just after they give their talks (Fig. 42). Here the graduate students will become better acquainted with their instructors in an informal atmosphere. Here the department head will find most of his staff assembled at one time, and he may be able to complete more items of business in five minutes than he could in his office in an hour. But most important of all, there is the chance for cross-fertilization of ideas among members of the staff.

The kitchenette attached to the common room deserves special consideration if it is to be of maximum usefulness without being too elaborate and expensive. The simplest version of such an arrangement is a niche in the wall, possibly 3 feet wide, 2 feet high, and 1 foot deep, provided with an electric outlet for a hotplate on one side and a combined faucet and drinking fountain with drainage area on the other. Storage space should be provided above, below, or nearby for equipment. A number of commercially manufactured units are available. The new mathematics building at Dartmouth contains a slightly more elaborate kitchenette unit, occupying an 11′ x 2′ area in a recess of the lounge, in which a refrigerator, stove, sink, and shelving for dishes and other equipment are provided (Fig. 43). Such an area could be separated from the rest of the lounge by a folding partition if desired. For institutions that can afford it, however, the best arrangement is to have a separate kitchenette in a room between 60 and 100 square feet, adjacent to but acoustically insulated from the lounge. This is particularly important if the lounge itself is to double as a colloquium room.

Colloquium room

Close to the common room or lounge there should be an adequately large colloquium room, which might also serve for certain classes. For smaller institutions the lounge itself may be assigned to serve also as a colloquium room. The colloquium room should have a large area of chalkboard on the front wall—two or three 6-foot wide sections, each with two or three vertically sliding counterbalanced panels, are suggested. It should be equipped with enough comfortable seats to accommodate all interested faculty and students who may attend an invited lecture by a guest speaker. The colloquium room should be equipped for the use of overhead projectors, slide projectors, and other audio-visual aids that may be suitable for a mathematics lecture. Well lighted and air conditioned, it should be a place in which it is a pleasure to speak and to listen. If the colloquium room is adjacent to the lounge, a folding partition might be used between these two rooms so that the lounge could seat an overflow audience for the colloquium lecture.

For institutions that may occasionally entertain larger regional or national meetings of mathematical organizations, it would be well to have available somewhere on campus two or three auditoriums seating 100 to 200, and one seating 500 persons. These auditoriums should be near each other and not too far from the mathematics department. Such facilities should be designed to be suitable not only for mathematics, but for other departments. The four auditoriums at the University of Michigan in the annex to Angell Hall, are an example of the type of facility ideal for mathematics meetings.

Lobbies and exhibit spaces

A visitor's first view of a mathematics building is likely to be in the lobby. It is important that this area be large enough to accommodate the student traffic and that it be attractively arranged. The lobby area is an ideal place to put mathematical exhibits either in an illuminated display case on the wall or in glass cases which may be viewed from all sides. Figure 44 shows an exhibit at the

Museum of Science and Industry that may suggest suitable displays for a mathematics lobby. The lobby should contain a directory of the offices in the building, as well as the room numbers of the departmental headquarters, the library, colloquium room, lounge, etc. In or near the lobby it would be appropriate to install a booth for a public telephone.

9 COMPUTATION CENTERS

Growth, organization, and function of campus computation centers

Computer technology is one of the fastest growing scientific developments of modern times.[7,53] The number of high-speed electronic digital computers in the United States was estimated at 5,000 in 1961 and was expected to double within two years! Fifteen years ago the modern digital computer did not exist. Ten years ago a computation center with electronic digital computers was a rarity on a college campus. In 1957, there were 29 centers participating in a survey of university computing activities. In 1961, over 150 college

FIGURE 44 *The IBM Mathematics exhibit, designed by Charles Eames, Museum of Science and Industry, Chicago*

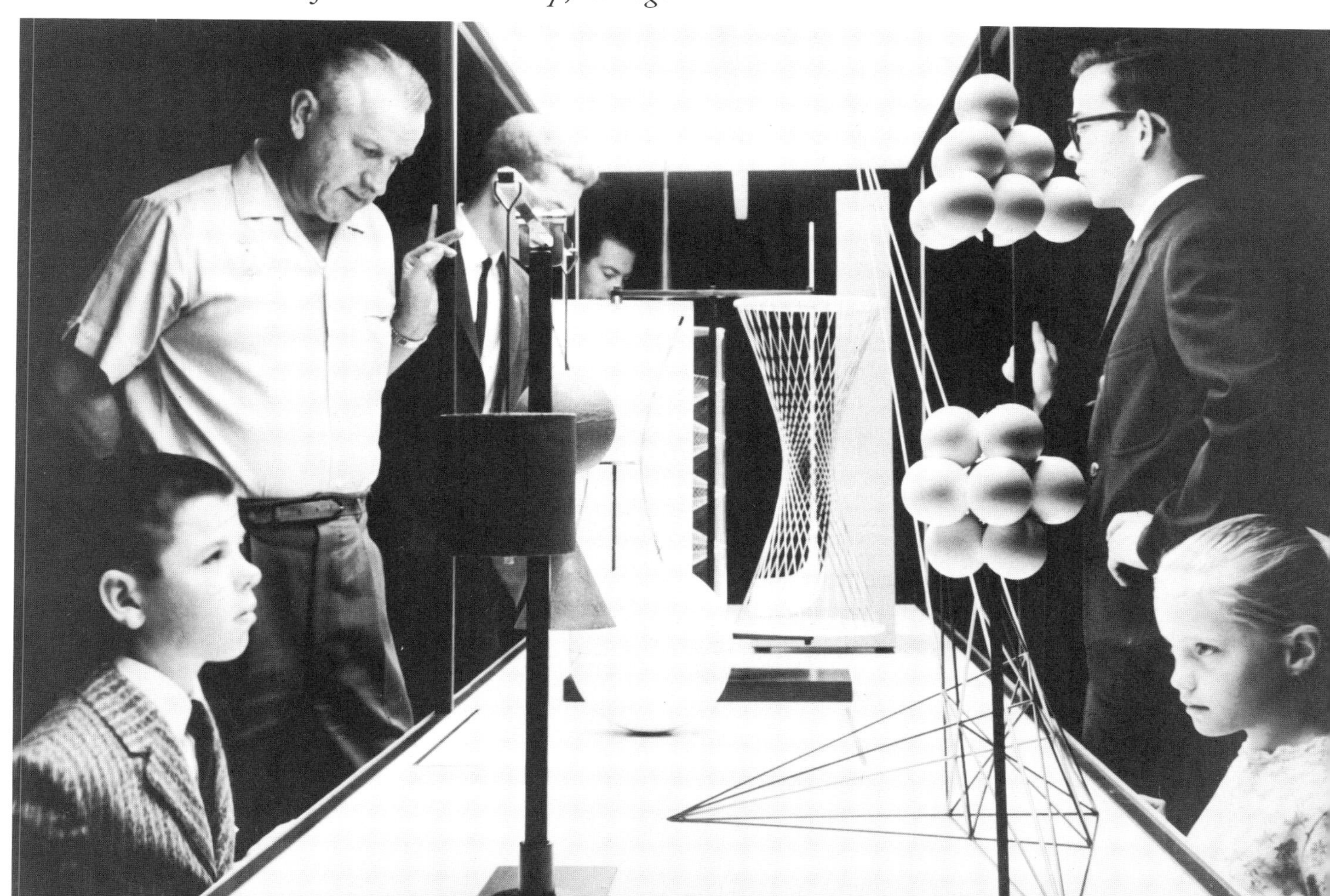

FIGURE 45 *High school students visiting the University of North Carolina (Chapel Hill) computer shown in the frontispiece*

campuses are reported to have such computer installations, of which 40 may be considered large installations (Fig. 45).[21] Both numbers may double within three to five years. Moreover, replies to the project questionnaire indicated that about 40 per cent of the existing facilities will be replaced or substantially enlarged within five years.

Most experts in the field agree that a computation center for a college or university should be an all-campus facility, administratively under the control either of the Graduate School or of an all-campus committee, rather than an adjunct of an academic department such as mathematics, statistics, or electrical engineering. Leadership from a single department or individual may be necessary for the establishment of the center, but the planning and ultimate control should provide for participation by all interested parties. A currently emerging pattern is the formation of a separate department of computer science with some teaching duties; it usually has some affiliation with the department of mathematics and is possibly not fully responsible for the service activities of the computation center.

Location of a computation center, public access, and parking

In choosing a central or peripheral location for a computer, the rapid development of computer use by medical schools, business schools, and behaviorial science groups, as well as by physical scientists and engineers, should be considered. Proximity to users must be weighed against the almost certain needs for expansion in the near future. New means are being developed whereby a fast central computer can service simultaneously a number of different input-output stations that may be placed strategically at several points on a campus.

A central location close to the main library tower was obtained for the University of Texas

Computation Center (Fig. 46), completed in September 1961, by building a one-story structure covered by an extension of the central terrace area where the ground drops off to a lower level. The building cost of $497,000 might have been reduced 20 per cent in a less central location, but the advantages obtained were considered worth the extra cost. At other institutions, a peripheral location is chosen because of the need for space to expand.

A computation center is visited daily by large numbers of people who come either as clients to have problems done on the computer or as visitors to see the facilities. Hence it is important that adequate parking be provided near the computation center to accommodate both its own staff and these visitors.

Access to the computer facilities must also be provided for the computing machinery and for the supplies that will be needed in its operation. It would be a sad mistake to build a fine room for a computer and then find that the machine itself could not be brought in, either because the doors were too small or the corridors, stairways, or elevators could not support the load.

The functions of a computation center may be different at different institutions, and must be considered in planning its location and space require-

FIGURE 46 *Main computer room, with observation area at the left, Computation Center, University of Texas*

ments. Among the possible objectives for a computer at a university might be: 1) to provide education and training in high-speed computation, by means of either regular academic courses or short courses in which the students actually use the computer; 2) to carry on research in the field of high-speed computing, including possibly such special areas as numerical analysis, advanced computer programing, artificial intelligence, language translation techniques; 3) to support research by faculty and students in areas other than computation itself; and 4) to assist neighboring industrial concerns in the solution of their computational problems and thereby provide some of the funds needed to support the university operations with the computer.

A small center with more limited objectives may require a relatively small amount of space at first. However, experience has often indicated that after a small computer has introduced research workers in many areas on the campus to the potentialities of computer use, a larger center is not only desired but justified. Wise planning must take this into account.

Furthermore, experience both on university campuses and in industrial organizations suggests that a single computer of great capability is preferable to a collection of several much slower machines, since both the machine cost and programing cost per unit of computing are cheaper on the single large machine than on several minor machines. It is assumed that the large machine is satisfactory to all parties concerned, is capable of handling the combined workload, and is not idle much of the time. The tenfold increase in cost required for a fast machine may possibly provide a hundredfold increase in capability, thereby reducing the *cost per unit of computing* by a factor of ten. This is a real saving if the fast machine is used to capacity, but not if it is used only 10 per cent of the time.

Perhaps even more serious than the direct dollar cost is the fragmentation of knowledge that takes place when each small computer has its own staff, communicating poorly, if at all, with similar groups on the same campus (see pp. 88–90). Despite this, groups frustrated by inconvenient or inadequate access press strongly and sometimes successfully for their own installation. A separate problem here is the need for analogue or digital equipment tied directly (i.e., "on line") to a real time experiment, such as a reactor, jet engine test stand, or a human being under some form of medical observation or treatment. Techniques for interrupting large-scale problems for brief uses of the computer are under very active development, but it is difficult at this time to predict whether additional machines of about the present size will be installed or whether even larger machines will be shared by many users, perhaps with the aid of off-site input and output devices.

Public viewing and briefing

The main computer room itself is an important showplace. Good public relations require that it be located where visitors can easily see it from a corridor or viewing room through a glass wall. Otherwise, there will be crowding that interferes with the work, as seen in Figure 45. A classroom, briefing room, or auditorium, equipped with adequate chalkboard in front, should be placed near the viewing area. This room can be used both for briefing groups who may come to see the computer and for regular instruction in computer science, either in short courses, institutes, or regular university courses.

Computer space

The main computer room is the heart of a computing center (Figs. 4, 46). It must be accessible to the computer staff who operate the machines and to the maintenance engineers who repair the machines and keep them in running order, as well as being strategically located for public viewing (Figs. 47, 48). It must also be accessible to appropriate storage spaces and to the power supply. Efficient operation requires that the individual machine units in the main computing room be so placed that they are easily accessible for quick repair in emergency, as well as being conveniently located for the operators and the public. If the distance from the back of the computer units to the walls were made 18 inches greater than the distance needed to open the cabinet doors and carry out repairs, this wall space could be used for storage that would be accessible except during maintenance. (However, fire regulations demand that only the absolute minimum of records required for efficient operation shall be kept in the computer room itself.) An upper limit to the distances between computer units may be set in some installations by the available lengths of information cable.

The machines in the main computer room need proper support, cable connections, and air conditioning. In the main machine rooms for most of the larger computers, the underlying fixed floor is built about 18 inches lower than the floors in adjacent preparation rooms or corridors, and it is covered by a strong elevated floor beneath which cable connections can be installed without obstructing the passageways (Fig. 49). Elevated floors are made by a number of commercial companies and commonly consist of a structural metal framework about 18 inches high, covered by square panels of flooring capable of supporting distributed loads of 250 pounds per square foot or concentrated loads of 1,000 pounds. The panels

FIGURE 47 *Plan of Computation Center, University of Texas*

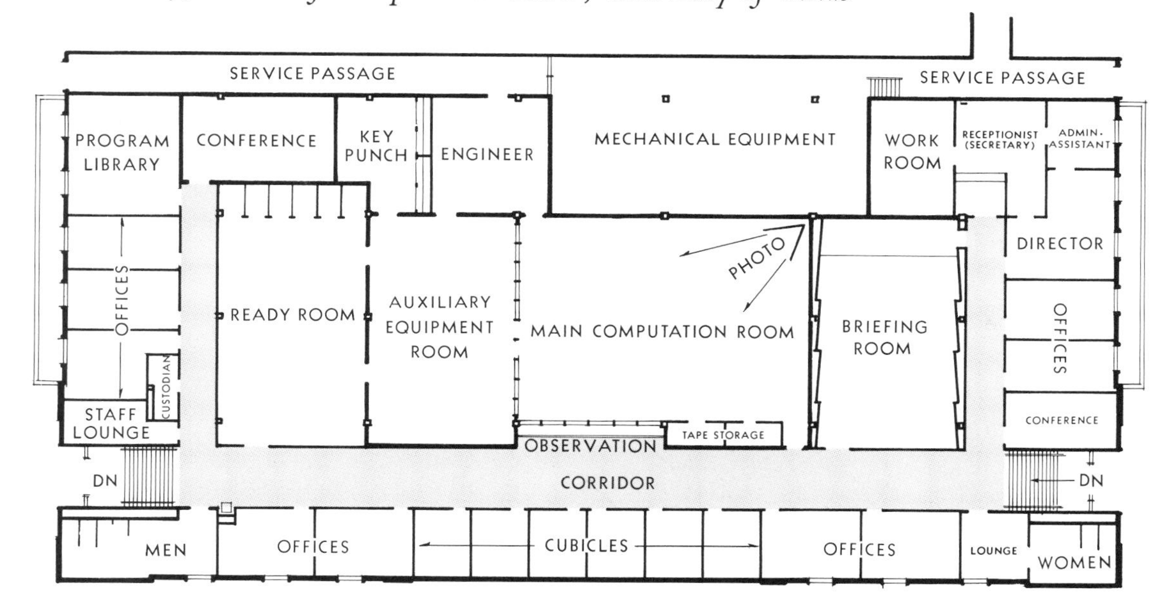

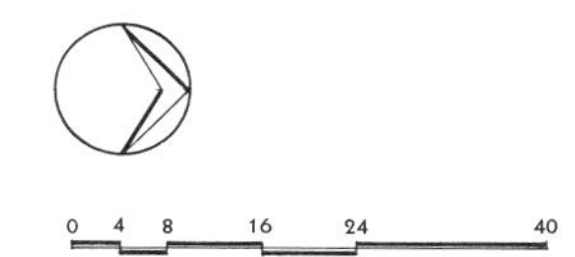

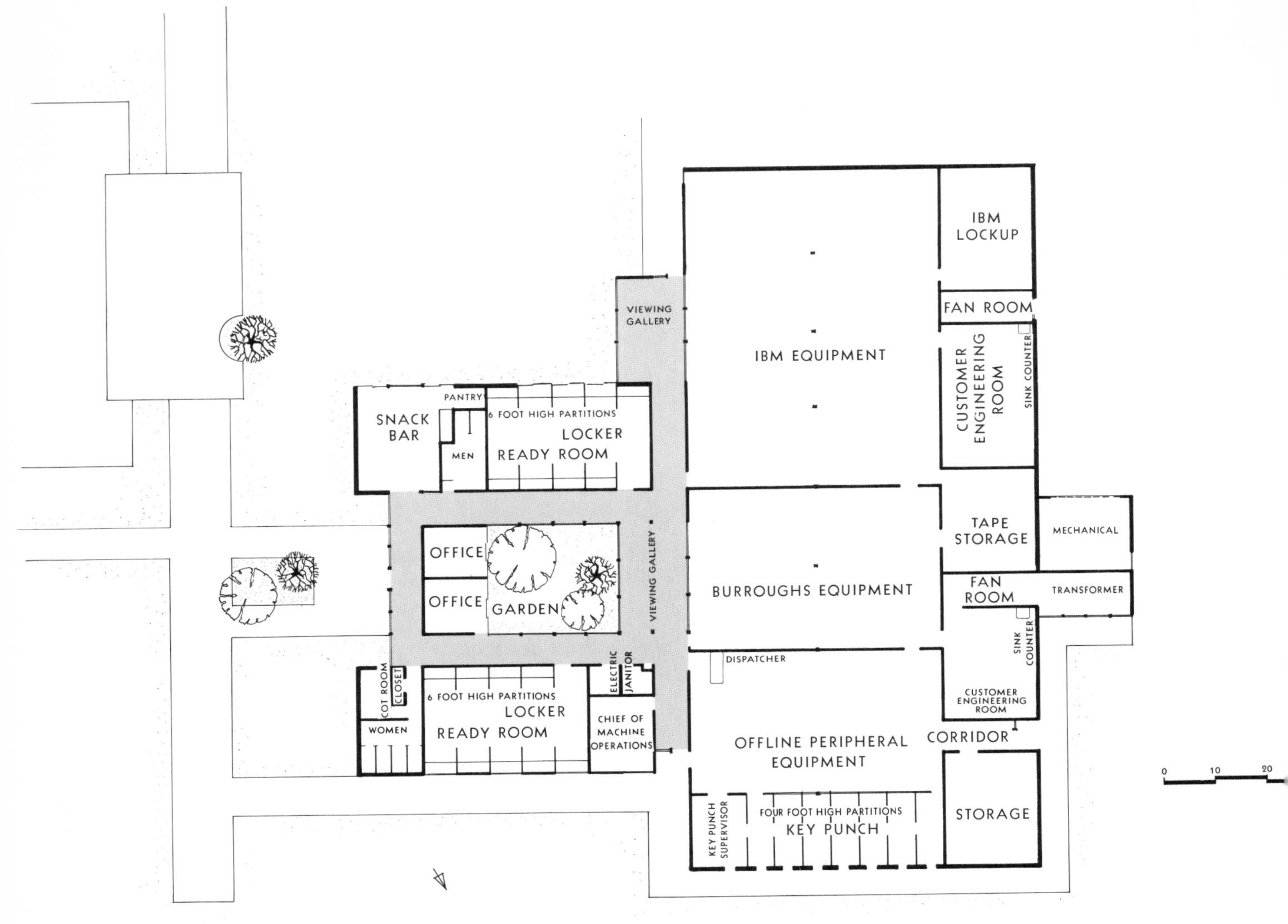

FIGURE 48 *Plan of Computation Center, Stanford University*

may be covered with carpeting or other types of flooring materials, but it is important that the floor be kept free from dust, lint, and static electricity. In buildings without a recessed subfloor, such as those remodeled for computer use, ramps should be used to connect the elevated floor with floor areas at a different level in order to permit carts with tape or punch cards, or other equipment, to be rolled in.

Some elevated floors are made airtight so that the space under the floor may also be used as a plenum for air conditioning to control the temperature and humidity in the machines. Cool air at about 68 degrees or less can be blown up through the machines to cool them and emerge in the room at a temperature of about 73 degrees, which is comfortable for the personnel. Temperature and relative humidity in the computer room should be continuously recorded by an easily viewed recording device that may be conveniently mounted on a wall. Such devices can be elaborate or relatively inexpensive, depending on requirements.

Auxiliary card-punch machines, tape preparation units, and printers may be included within the vapor seal enclosing the main computer units, but should probably be separated from the main room by glass panels to reduce the noise level and dirt. Acoustic treatment of the ceilings is important for noise reduction. Adequate and well-diffused lighting should also be installed in the ceilings of the computer areas.

For reasons of fire protection it is important to avoid cluttering the computer room with the storage of combustible materials not needed in the day-to-day activity of the computer. However, some information storage media, such as punched Hollerith cards, punched tape, or magnetic tape, are needed for current use and should be readily accessible; a fireproof storage closet for such items should be adjacent to the computer room. Magnetic tapes are commonly stored in flat, cylindrical cans, placed on racks so that their circular bases are in a vertical plane. Metal file cabinets with drawers designed for standard punched cards are also commercially available.

Maintenance and mechanical areas, power, and air conditioning

Adequate space should be provided near the main equipment room for the use of maintenance engineers, whether they be local personnel or representatives of the equipment manufacturer on contract to repair the machines. Undue economy in the space available to maintenance engineers may be no economy at all in the long run, since time wasted in repairing a fast computer may be worth several dollars a minute.

Spaces for auxiliary mechanical equipment for the computer, including the power supply and air conditioning, must be provided close to the main computer room. There are some advantages in having this area adjacent to the working areas for maintenance personnel.

Preparation areas

Electronic digital computers are built to perform

FIGURE 49 *Elevated floor for a computation center*

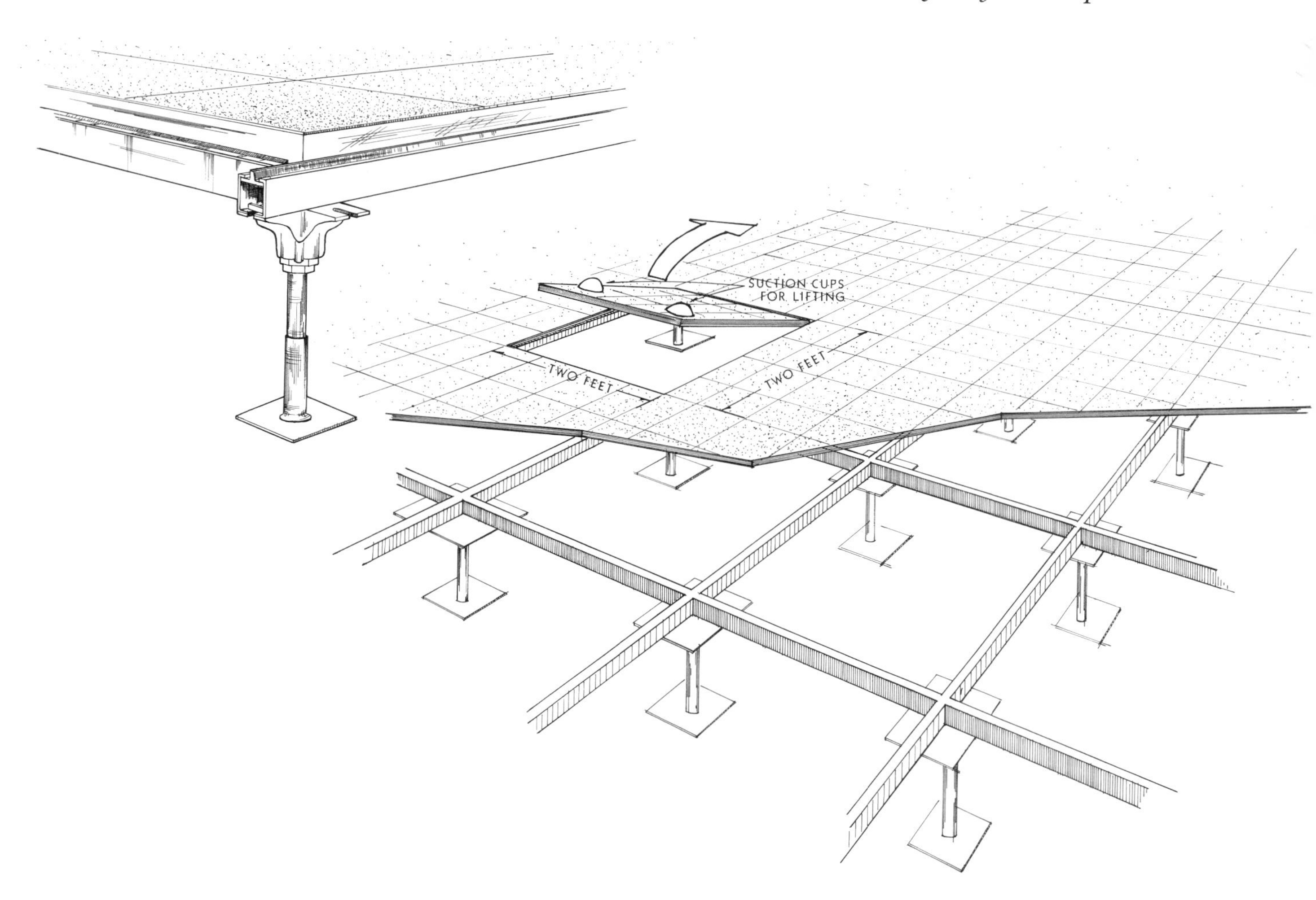

a succession of simple arithmetical or logical operations at very high speed in accordance with instructions given in a program. Some are so fast that they can do a million or more of these operations in one second. However, they must obey detailed instructions that tell them after each operation what is to be done next. Preparing these lists of instructions is called "programing."

Before a program can be run on a digital computer, the original problem must first be formulated mathematically, and the steps in its solution must be described in a general way in a flow diagram. Details must then be filled in, which convert the flow diagram into a set of instructions for the computer. These instructions must then be placed on cards or tape in a form that the computer can read.

For this work there should be a preparation room, or "ready room," near the auxiliary machine room, where programers may put their programs on tape or cards that the computer can read, and where they may check their programs for errors. Fortunately or unfortunately, an electronic digital computer does just what the program tells it to do, rather than what the programer may have intended the program to tell it to do. Errors are regularly made in programing that must be corrected before the program will work as intended. The process of finding these errors, known as "debugging," may be quite time-consuming. It may involve giving part or all of a program a trial run on the machine and comparing machine answers, or the contents of certain memory positions at certain stages of the calculation, with what would be expected if all went well. These expected values may in certain cases be obtained by an approximate computation carried out on a desk calculator. Thus, a ready room should be equipped with work tables and desk calculators in addition to the auxiliary punch units that may be needed for preparing programs to be read by the computer. Well-run computer installations currently set aside several periods each day when such "debugging" runs may be scheduled. For efficient operation, many people who do not have permanent offices in the computer area need temporary work space there.

A reception desk or counter may be provided in or near the ready room to accept and check in programs to be run on the machine, record completed work, and return it to an appropriate cubbyhole in a large rack, where it may be picked up by the person who submitted it.

Offices, conference rooms, library, and lounge

Spaces required by the computer personnel, in addition to the preparation areas just described, include offices, conference rooms, library, and lounge or refreshment corner. Conference rooms are needed in which several persons, including the proposer of the problem, may get together to discuss possible methods of attack for its solution. Private offices are needed where people working on problems can concentrate without interruption on the complicated series of steps necessary to program a problem.

A reference library should be readily available to computer personnel (see p. 88). This library should include not only a collection or "library" of subroutines and other programs that may be stored on tape or punched cards, but also at least a minimal collection of technical books and journals relating to computing and numerical analysis. A larger departmental collection in a separate room, including duplicates of some pertinent mathematics books, may be justified if the computing center cannot share a library with mathematics or statistics and is not near the main library.

Offices for computer personnel should include the same essentials as for mathematics professors, namely, a desk, chairs, bookshelving, telephone, and adequate chalkboard on at least one wall. However, the computer specialist may have more need than the pure mathematician for electrical equipment such as a desk calculator or a tape punch. These require electrical outlets and either a table or writing shelf on which to work.

Regular staff members of a computer center should not only have individual offices where they can work without distraction, but also a staff lounge where they can get together to exchange ideas and charge their mental batteries. At the University of Texas Computation Center (Fig. 47), ten offices of 180 square feet each and six cubicles of 100 square feet each are provided for the use of staff and graduate students, and there is a small lounge in which coffee can be served. Since a computer may be in operation 24 hours a day, and programing activities require long periods of meticulous work, a kitchenette or at least a hot plate may be needed to restore the energy and efficiency of the staff.

Reception, administration, duplicating, and storage

The administrative space for the computing center may closely resemble the administrative space for a mathematics department. Not to be forgotten are offices for the director and his assistant, office space for reception and for secretaries and typists, and a workroom equipped with duplicating machines and plenty of shelving space for all the reports and notes that must be reproduced. Of course, adequate space with controlled temperature and humidity must be provided for the storage of punched cards. Clearly, such general facilities as toilets must not be overlooked.

A computer installation uses large quantities of materials, such as punch cards, paper tapes, ditto paper, and paper for a high-speed printer. Suitable provision must be made for receiving and storing these supplies. Inadequate storage space is not the best reason for inhibiting the output of high-speed printers whose copy may "flow" from the machine at the rate of 600 or more 120-character lines per minute. Printing by machine at slower speeds directly on multilith masters permits the reproduction of computer-produced information without the errors arising from human intervention. Supplies for such work will require storage (see check list in Appendix).

Fire protection and emergencies

To prevent damage to the computer by fire or water hazards arising outside the computer room itself, the equipment should be housed in a fire-resistive building and should be protected by fire doors from the rest of the building; the flooring should be of noncombustible construction, and the roof or floor above the computer room should be a watertight slab to which the walls are sealed. Waterproofed walls and proper drainage may be needed to prevent water damage in a basement installation. Local fire protection for certain key computer units may be provided by approved automatic carbon dioxide fire extinguishers rather than by water sprinklers. Cards, disks, and drums should be kept in waterproof, noncombustible metal cabinets with controlled temperature and humidity, if required. Those not in current use should be stored in a separate room close to the computer room. Magnetic tape itself is highly flammable. Duplicate copies of programs and records might be stored in a remote place as insurance against their total loss by a fire in the computer center. Adequate controls should prevent the ducts of the computer air-conditioning system from circulating smoke and fire in case of emergency; it is best to have the computer air ducts independent of the other air ducts in the building. All office furniture in the computer room should be metal. Details concerning the protection of computer systems from fire are published in a "Standard for the Protection of Electronic Computer Systems" (1962 NFPA reports, pp. 223–249).[38]

Hazards other than fire and water that may need to be considered in planning and maintaining a computer installation are those from radiation, magnetic fields, static electricity, dust, insects, or rodents. To protect stored rolls of magnetic tape from loss of information due to local magnetic disturbances, it is best to place their containers on edge in a magnetically protected storage place. To minimize the effects of dust and static electricity, carpets and drapes should be made of materials free from lint and static; the use of dust cloths or dry mops for cleaning should be avoided.

Plans for the use of alternate computer facilities in case of emergency should be worked out in advance and should be known by all the regular computer personnel.

If the incoming power supply for the computer is subject to occasional interruptions, a secondary source of power may be needed to provide continuity of operations. Failure of the air-conditioning system may also cause the computer to shut down within a short time, so there should be a warning alarm that will immediately call attention to such a failure.

LFFT *Early laboratory, woodcut, 1503.*
BELOW *Modern laboratory between two classrooms.*

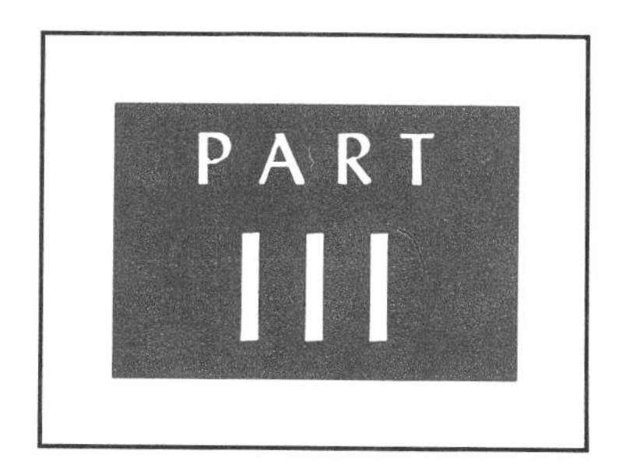

MATHEMATICAL FACILITIES FOR SECONDARY EDUCATION

Part Three analyzes the needs for space and facilities for mathematical instruction in secondary schools. These needs are examined in the light of enrollment trends, teacher shortages, course content improvement studies, and new instructional procedures; the needs include appropriate facilities for classroom instruction, mathematical laboratories and areas for individual study, library, storage and preparation areas, and offices for teachers and departmental administration.

10 MATHEMATICAL FACILITIES FOR SECONDARY EDUCATION

Enrollments and teacher supply in high school mathematics

Arithmetic, algebra, and geometry have for generations played an important role in the curriculum of elementary and secondary schools in the United States. In 1900 nearly all students enrolled in high school studied two years of algebra and one of plane geometry, but these courses were partially replaced as a much larger percentage of boys and girls of high school age completed four years of secondary school. General mathematics was offered instead of algebra for a considerable percentage of non-college-bound 9th, as well as 10th, 11th, and 12th, graders. As high school enrollments increased by a factor of 20 in 60 years, a smaller percentage of students took algebra and geometry. Whereas 56.9 per cent of all pupils enrolled in the last four years of public high schools were enrolled in algebra in 1910 and 30.9 per cent in geometry, these percentages dropped to 30.4 for algebra and 17.1 for geometry in 1934, and to 24.6 for algebra and 11.6 for geometry in 1952–53.[6] Then an awakening interest in science and mathematics, together with an increasing awareness of the importance of mathematics in the education of both the scientist and nonscientist, reversed the downward trend in algebra and geometry. In a randomly selected sample of 4,254 high schools studied in a recent report of the U.S. Office of Education, nearly two-thirds of the high school principals stated that their schools were giving more emphasis to mathematics than three years earlier, about one-third indicated the same emphasis, and fewer than 1 per cent indicated less emphasis. Expressed as a percentage of the grade where the course is usually given, the enrollments in mathematics courses changed from 1954 to 1958 as follows:[6]

	1954	*1958*
General mathematics	44.5	34.4
Elementary algebra	64.5	71.6
Plane geometry	37.4	44.7
Intermediate algebra	28.5	37.0
Solid geometry	6.5	3.9
Plane trigonometry	7.4	11.5

The fact that the sum of the enrollments in general mathematics and elementary algebra exceeds 100 per cent of the ninth grade enrollment is due to the fact that some students from other grades were enrolled in these courses; many enroll in general mathematics before elementary algebra. It should also be noted that although solid geometry as a separate course was offered in fewer schools in 1958 than before and had been deemphasized in favor of other topics in mathematics, some instruction in solid geometry was beginning to be included in the plane geometry course. Solid geometry was no longer used as a primary vehicle for teaching deductive proof, but the development of space concepts was, and is still, considered important.

The supply of teachers adequately trained in mathematics has increased considerably in the last decade, but has not caught up with the demand created by the growing enrollments in high school mathematics. A research report of the National Education Association on Teacher Supply and Demand in Public Schools, 1962,[60] states that the number of mathematics majors graduating from college with a secondary school teacher's certificate was 4,618 in 1950, 2,155 in 1955 (the low point), 6,124 in 1961, and 7,001 (estimated) in 1962. Of the 6,124 men and women in the 1961 group, 75.3 per cent entered secondary school teaching in 1961–62, 5.8 per cent accepted other gainful employment, 0.9 per cent were seeking employment, 6.7 per cent continued formal study,

4.9 per cent entered military service (men) or homemaking (women), and 6.4 per cent gave no information. Replies from 29 states and the District of Columbia to a questionnaire about teacher supply and demand in various fields indicated that in mathematics the teacher *demand* (3,857 new teachers employed whose principal assignment was teaching mathematics) exceeded by 24.3 per cent the *supply* (3,104 trained in these states out of the total of 6,124 mathematics majors graduating in the United States with teaching certificates). Since only about 75 per cent of this "supply" actually entered teaching and the recruitment of former mathematics majors after military service or graduate training could make up for only a part of the 1961 "supply" that did not enter teaching, there must have been a substantial number of persons employed in 1961–62 to teach mathematics who did not have adequate preparation in mathematics.

Fast-growing opportunities for mathematicians in industry, with high starting salaries, often lure mathematics teachers and prospective teachers away from the high school. Those who choose mathematics teaching as a career do not do so mainly to make money. The best are enthusiastic about young people; they are enthusiastic about mathematics and want to communicate their enthusiasm to others. Proper facilities, including classrooms, offices, and study areas, are an important means of keeping alive this enthusiasm and creating the environment in which it will be fruitful in stimulating young minds into exciting intellectual adventures.

The changing mathematics curriculum in elementary and secondary schools, its relation to the overall school program, and its implications for the physical environment

The late 1950's marked the beginnings of a revolution in the teaching of mathematics, concentrated at first in the high school curriculum and later extended downward into the elementary schools and upward into the colleges. The new programs emphasize the "why" of mathematics along with the "how." They aim to produce a higher degree of mathematical literacy among students at all levels and a better understanding of the structure and logic of mathematical and scientific reasoning. Basic concepts are stressed along with manipulative skills.

There is no single nationally accepted program for the new approach to mathematics. Instead, several groups have been working separately with similar aims to develop new programs of instruction in mathematics, emphasizing the structure of mathematics and an understanding of its basic principles. The School Mathematics Study Group (SMSG) was started in 1958 under the direction of Professor E. G. Begle, with support from the National Science Foundation. Assisted by at least 100 mathematicians and 100 high school teachers, it first produced and widely tested sample textbooks for grades 7–12, and more recently it prepared mathematics materials to be used in grades 4, 5, 6. The University of Illinois Committee on School Mathematics (UICSM), directed by Dr. Max Beberman, has prepared and tested texts for grades 9–12, emphasizing the role of pupil discovery in understanding mathematical principles. The University of Maryland Mathematics Project (UMMaP), directed by Dr. John R. Mayor, undertook to develop an improved mathematics program for grades 7 and 8, to serve as a bridge between arithmetic and high school mathematics, and tested their materials with the help of more than 100 teachers in several states. Additional efforts to improve high school mathematics have been undertaken by other groups. Among these are the Boston College Mathematics Institute under Dr. Stanley J. Bezuszka, S. J. (grades 8–12), and the Ball State Teachers College Experimental Program under Dr. Charles Brumfiel (grades 7–

12), the Commission on Mathematics of the College Entrance Examination Board,[50] and the Developmental Project in Secondary Mathematics of Southern Illinois University. The National Council of Teachers of Mathematics appointed a Secondary School Curriculum Committee which in turn appointed 11 subcommittees to study various aspects of the problem of curriculum reorganization. One of these committees prepared a pamphlet entitled, "A Guide to the Use and Procurement of Teaching Aids in Mathematics," which contains classroom plans and sources of a variety of teaching aids.[4] The National Council has also prepared a booklet entitled, "The Revolution in School Mathematics," which describes in some detail the salient features of these various programs.[63]

A number of other groups besides the School Mathematics Study Group have been preparing mathematics materials for the elementary school. The Greater Cleveland Mathematics Program, directed by Bernard H. Gundlach, is publishing materials for grades K-6. Professors Patrick Suppes and Newton S. Hawley of Stanford University have been working respectively on materials in Sets and Numbers, and in Geometry, appropriate for use by elementary school students. For the Madison project, Dr. Robert Davis of Syracuse University has written materials suitable for presentation in upper elementary or junior high school. Materials will soon be available at all levels in the elementary school for teachers with adequate mathematical background.

At the college level the drive to revise the mathematics curriculum is being spearheaded by the Committee on the Undergraduate Program in Mathematics (CUPM) of the Mathematical Association of America.[11] It is not expected that a final blueprint of the curriculum at all levels will be found that is satisfying to everyone and will never be changed again. On the contrary, it is felt that as knowledge expands and new concepts and techniques become important in the training of scientists, a continuing revision of the curriculum may be necessary to keep it up to date.

Mathematics is not the only subject area that is working on curriculum improvement. As new programs are introduced in the various fields, an attempt should be made to coordinate the ideas into an overall educational program. Particularly in closely related disciplines, like physics and mathematics, the teachers in one field should be kept informed of what the others are expecting of their pupils.

The implementation of a new mathematics program in the school system requires more than an agreement by the authorities that a change is desirable and indeed long overdue. Adequate preparation of teachers is an essential first step. The opportunity for teachers to continue their training in both the new subject-matter and methods of presentation must be provided on a long-range basis. They will need books and materials to study and time to study. They will need a place, separate from the eating rooms, where they may study or exchange ideas and experiences with their colleagues. A facility provided at some schools is a teachers' room for possibly six or more teachers in which each has a desk, file, and bookshelf. This is certainly better than no teachers' room at all, but it may provide neither privacy for study and student conferences nor a suitable area for group conferences with teachers. A possible arrangement is shown in Figure 57. An arrangement with some private offices for teachers and a departmental office for group meetings (Fig. 55) would be better.

Suitable space for teachers is one implication of the new programs in mathematics. There are other implications for facilities required by teachers and students in mathematics. Programed curricula and an increased supply of audio-visual materials require appropriate facilities for their use. Special programs for the gifted student in mathematics and the emphasis on discovery and independent investigation by all students may require appropriate facilities. Students must have access to a number of books and papers for outside reading in connection with the new instructional materials. The School Mathematics Study Group is sponsoring the writing of a new mathematical library, to consist of more than 30 books, suitable for supplementary reading by high school students, teachers, and the generally educated lay public. Commercial publishers are also producing a variety of pamphlets, books, charts, and films related to the proposals of current curriculum groups. Some of these books and instructional materials should be made available in the school library. Some should be brought to the attention of students by being displayed on shelves in the classroom.

Activities of teachers and students in mathematics and the spaces required. Team teaching

Specific designs of space for a mathematics department should take account of the functions of the chairman, teacher, and student in the educational process, the types of learning and teaching activities to be performed, and the available supplies. Spaces will include classrooms, laboratories, library, and other instructional spaces, as well as offices, conference rooms, and storage spaces.[3,19,22,42] Some of these spaces should be flexible enough to provide for multiple use in the same term, or for changing uses in different terms. If possible, new facilities should be so built that they will be adaptable for unforeseen future needs.[35]

The chairman of a high school mathematics department of more than two or three teachers may have duties associated with the planning of the curriculum, the acquisition of mathematics books and teaching aids, the hiring of new teachers, the supervision of instruction and personnel, in-service training, and many routine administrative duties requiring the assistance of a department secretary and technical aide. He certainly needs an office with room for a desk, files, books, a telephone, and a few chairs for visitors. If possible, he should have a private office adjoining the department office, and appropriate space for a secretary, either in the department office or in an office next to the chairman. He should have access to a room suitable for holding conferences with teachers, students, or parents.

The primary duty of a high school mathematics teacher is the preparation and teaching of classes. Other important duties are the evaluation of student performance, the holding of conferences, the evaluation of new texts, and professional self-improvement. Class preparation and teaching now may require the planning and production of demonstrations and presentations using audio-visual aids, and the preparing and duplication of worksheets and laboratory guides. Student evaluation includes the preparing and grading of assignments and examinations, and the recording of grades. Conferences may be held with individual students, teachers, chairman, principal, counselors, and parents. The evaluation of new texts may require background reading and study of many of the new books and pamphlets concerned with mathematics instruction in the high school. Professional self-improvement will mean independent study and may involve attendance at in-service meetings.

Teachers need appropriate spaces not only for teaching but also for their other duties. If possible, each teacher should have a separate office for work that requires privacy, and he should be able to share a department office for group discussion, reading, and relaxation.

If space is not available to assign private offices, then each teacher should at least have his own desk, file, and bookshelf in a department office, and there should be suitable space nearby for group discussions among teachers and for private

FIGURE 50 *Large classroom, Cubberley Senior High School, Palo Alto, California*

conferences with parents or students (Fig. 57).

Learning activities of the students for which provision should be made are principally of the following types: a) group learning, discussions, demonstration, exploration, and discovery; b) independent study, including library reading and research, independent assignments or project work, the completion of make-up assignments or tests, and the use of teaching machines or programed texts; c) laboratory work, including the making of models, charts, and equipment, and the preparation of demonstrations and exhibits; d) computational work, involving the operation of slide rules, desk calculators, or computing machines; and e) preparation and use of audio-visual material and viewing of television films.

Recent developments in team teaching imply different uses of space by both teachers and students from the traditional pattern of one teacher in a classroom for 25–35 students.[48,49] Under one plan of team teaching, several teachers are jointly responsible for a group of 50 to 100 students. Members of the team may take turns presenting materials to a large group of students in a large lecture room (Fig. 50) or by television to smaller rooms; while one teacher is lecturing, the other team members may attend the lecture, supervise the listening group, or use this time as a preparation period. For blocks of time the large group is divided into small groups for questions, discussion, and oral or written testing. A substantial part of each week may be utilized by students for individual study, problem solving, and outside reading. Individual study stations offer the ideal facility for the latter type of work, provided that these stations are accessible to the reading materials required. In another type of team teaching situation, two classrooms for 30 students each are separated by a folding partition, so that without changing rooms it is possible to present to the whole group at once a portion of the instruction which adapts itself to a large group presentation, and to present the remainder of the lesson in small groups. This has the advantage that 1) students do not have to move from one room to another, and 2) the division of time between large group and small group activities is more flexible, as students and teachers are not forced to stay in a particular room because of scheduling difficulties.

Size and furnishings of classrooms for mathematics[3,57,69]

The size of a mathematics classroom is determined by two major factors: the number of students to be accommodated and the types of activity for which the room is used. If the classroom is used only for presentation and discussion, a room of 600–800 square feet may be adequate for a class of 30 pupils. A larger area is needed if a reading alcove of 100 square feet and a work area of comparable size are to be included. Individual project work in mathematics may be carried on by the students in a separate laboratory or workroom, or it may be carried on in the classroom itself if an appropriate area of 100 to 300 square feet in the classroom is provided for this purpose. The classroom need not be rectangular. Spaces for workroom activity, a reading alcove, and a teachers' alcove, may be separated from the main classroom area either by permanent walls reaching to the ceiling or by lower room dividers.[3] Such dividers might have bulletin board space on one side and bookshelves on the other, or they might consist of hinged panels of chalkboard.

The major features to be provided in the classroom proper are as follows:

1. Adequate seating for teacher and pupils.
2. Adequate chalkboard and good quality chalk.
3. Facilities for active displays.
4. Facilities for passive displays.
5. Projection equipment, with storage for projector and equipment, screens, and electrical outlets.
6. Sufficient storage for class materials and equipment, and for teachers' and students' belongings.
7. Miscellaneous equipment, such as pencil sharpeners, coat rack, basin or sink.
8. Adequate provision for light, acoustics, and ventilation.

The teacher who uses the same classroom for several periods in the day should have a desk with sufficient drawer space, a bookcase, and a file where restricted materials like examinations may be locked. In any case, a teacher should have either a desk or table, a comfortable desk chair for his own use, and storage space for personal belongings (Fig. 51). Some teachers would like a movable demonstration cart. A large electric clock should be visible, preferably on the rear wall. Student stations should have enough writing space. If tablet armchairs are provided, the writing surface should be large, and there should be space under the seat for placing papers and books. It should not be overlooked that right-handed tablet armchairs are somewhat awkward for left-handed writers. Many high school mathematics teachers feel that fixed tablet armchairs are unsatisfactory. If student stations are provided in combined desk-chair units, the seat and desk heights should be adjustable, or at least be comfortable for all students in the class. Many teachers prefer individual desk-chair units. Some prefer an arrangement by which pupils are seated two at a table, because this requires less floor space and may allow a larger writing surface per person and more space to set down books and papers. Others protest that an arrangement with two at a table encourages student conversations during class and collaboration during examinations. A formica writing surface is generally preferred to the traditional wooden desk.

Most mathematics teachers feel that the best visual aid for teaching mathematics is an adequate amount of well-surfaced, well-lighted chalkboard, mounted so that it can be easily used and viewed. Because of the importance of chalkboards and chalk to the mathematician, they will be discussed at some length in Part IV. The classroom teacher of mathematics who does not use the overhead projector to the complete exclusion of chalkboards likes to have a large chalkboard surface at the front of the room. Teachers who like to send some or all of the class to the board at once to do problems would insist on having chalkboards on two or three sides of the room, if possible. Some might like the arrangement of mathematics classrooms at the U. S. Air Force Academy, where chalkboards are provided on all four walls (Fig. 52). Vertically rising chalkboards provide the best visibility. Horizontally rolling

FIGURE 51 *Teacher's closet in mathematics classroom, Natick (Mass.) High School*

FIGURE 52 *Mathematics classroom, U. S. Air Force Academy, Colorado*

boards allow more chalkboard space than fixed boards on a given wall surface, and permit the use of a map rail for hanging display materials, coordinate grids, and a variety of visual aids. A thin strip of tackboard above the map rail provides for the display of pictures and drawings.

Various coordinate grids will be discussed in Part IV (p. 141). Facilities for other active displays in the classroom are considered under visual aids (p. 130). Items considered include a properly mounted demonstration slide rule (p. 131), objects hung from a map rail over the chalkboard, models or books supported on pegboards, and the graphing of points and lines using either pegboards or magnets on a steel chalkboard. Film and slide projectors and overhead projectors with their screens are also discussed at greater length in Part IV. They should be remembered in designing a high school classroom for mathematics, insofar as they involve built-in features like electrical outlets and mountings.

Facilities are needed for all sorts of display materials that are not actively used in class instruction, but serve as supplementary aids to learning. Pictures of famous mathematicians might be displayed either on a strip of bulletin board over the front chalkboard, on some other classroom wall, or in the corridor. One glass-enclosed cabinet should be provided in a mathematics classroom for the display of solid models and other materials that cannot be posted on a bulletin board or are too valuable to be handled. This cabinet could be combined in a single unit with drawer space underneath. Bulletin board space is needed to display printed materials, such as interesting facts about mathematics, weekly problems to challenge the better students, information about professional opportunities in mathematics, and student drawings or other exhibits. These displays are described in the booklet "How To Use Your Bulletin Board," published by the National Council of Teachers of Mathematics.[26]

Storage space of many varieties is needed in a modern mathematics classroom. This includes at least ten 6-foot shelves for magazines and books. It should also include built-in storage drawers for papers and materials; some of the drawers should be large and flat for charts and drawings (Fig. 58). If electric desk calculators or electric teaching machines are used in the classroom, there must not only be electrical outlets available, but locking cabinets in which to store the machines. These machines should be on rolling stands. An overhead projector itself is a valuable piece of equipment and cannot be left where it will be tampered with by the curious. It should be mounted on a movable stand or cabinet (Fig. 61), with storage for extra lights, extension cords, and supplies, such as grease pencils, extra transparencies, and cleaning materials (p. 143). There should be a storage closet or cabinet either in the classroom or in a nearby equipment and preparation room in which the projector can be safely stored.

Some schools provide individual drawers where students may store their papers, books, and drawing instruments, or special equipment and materials used in student projects (Fig. 58).

Either in the classrooms, in the department office, or in a separate duplicating and preparation room, facilities should be provided for using and storing duplicating machines and related equipment and supplies.

Besides these major items, a number of other items should not be overlooked. Provision should be made for hanging coats and hats of both teacher and pupils, either in the classroom or some other suitable place. Enough pencil sharpeners should be provided so that the class does not have to queue up and waste valuable time before each written exercise. A reading alcove in a classroom should be a nook of at least 100 square feet, equipped with a table and chairs and surrounded by bookshelves where mathematics books and magazines are made available for supplementary reading. A basin or sink in a front corner of the room near the chalkboard may not be considered essential, but it would be appreciated by a teacher who makes heavy use of the chalkboard.

Large lecture presentations

In recent years a number of high school mathematics teachers have experimented with large-group instruction either by large lecture sections or by television. Some have felt this approach necessary as a means of coping with larger enrollments during a critical shortage of qualified teachers. Others have felt it advisable as a more efficient use of teacher time. With more time to prepare, master teachers will raise the quality of education by giving better presentations to more boys and girls. One pattern of team teaching is for a master teacher to present certain topics in expert fashion to a large group composed of several classes, and for his presentation to be followed up by class discussions in small groups under the guidance of possibly less expert teachers, who improve their own techniques by watching the master teacher perform.

Another pattern is to have four teachers of approximately equal ability share responsibility for four homogeneously grouped classes; each meets his own class two or three times a week for discussion and problem solving; and each takes a turn at presenting a unified portion of the subject-matter in two or three consecutive lectures to the whole group in a large lecture room, while the other teachers are present but not actively involved. Each teacher is on his mettle under such circumstances to give a polished performance.

Each has three out of four weeks when he meets his own small group, but does not have such lectures to prepare, and can spend part of the released time in professional reading and self-improvement. Still another pattern involves joint activity by two teachers whose adjoining classrooms are separated by a folding partition, and can be combined into a larger room for 60 for appropriate portions of the instruction (Figs. 27, 53).

The large lecture method of instruction presupposes a suitable classroom arrangement, with a big chalkboard or an overhead projector (or both) in front (Fig. 50), and with seats arranged so that all may see well; with a microphone and amplification system and good acoustical design, so that all may hear well; and with adequate ventilation and temperature control, so that all may remain reasonably alert. In one high school, the disturbance caused by latecomers climbing over the laps of others is avoided by having four individual seats for latecomers in front by the doorway (Fig. 50). Placement of the door in the back of the room would avoid this difficulty.

Seats in a large lecture room should not all be at the same level. If rows of seats are spaced 3 feet apart, a rise of 6 inches per row should assure good visibility. Even a rise of only 3 or 4 inches per row should be adequate, if seats are staggered in alternate rows.

The large lecture room should be designed to permit the use of one or two overhead projectors, with screens mounted to permit good visibility without distortion. Conduits should be installed to permit the use of closed-circuit television, and there should be provision for showing films or filmstrips, or slides, if desired.

Mathematics laboratories, workrooms and computing rooms

Active student participation is an important feature of a good program of instruction in mathematics. In a subject like mathematics, learning is facilitated if a student not merely sees and hears mathematics being done by the teacher, but also participates actively himself in a variety of learning activities. Teachers differ in the type of activity they recommend for their pupils. Some

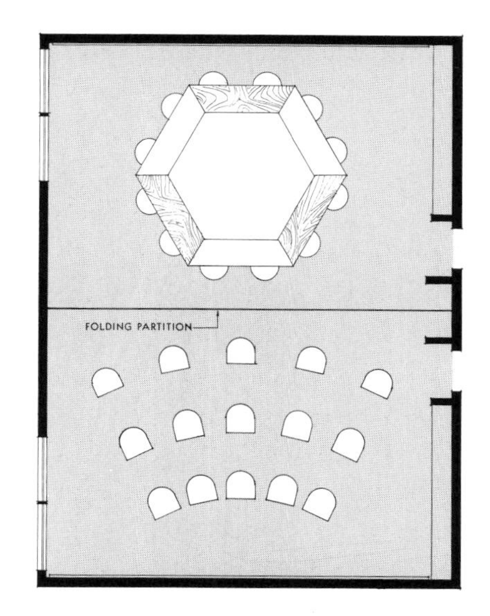

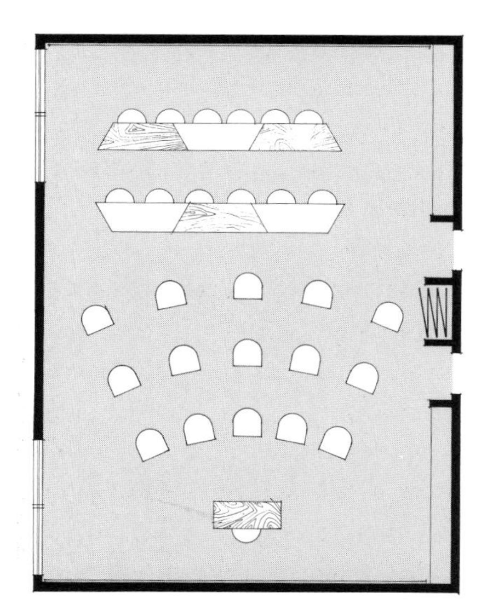

FIGURE 53 *A classroom, divisible into two seminar rooms*

FIGURE 54 *Mathematics laboratory between two classrooms, Fridley (Minn.) Senior High School*

may assign individual projects, part of which may involve independent research, collection of data, measurement activities, drawing of figures, and making of models. Others may wish to stress computational problems requiring the use of a desk calculator or possibly even in rare cases a high-speed digital computer. Occasionally a group of high school students may build their own digital computers.

Mathematics laboratories of at least four different types are found in high schools. The simplest "laboratory" is an alcove of a classroom equipped with a work table, tools, and instruments, where students may make drawings, exhibits, demonstrations, or models, or carry on a variety of individual projects. A more adequate facility like the one in the Fridley Senior High School, Minnesota (Fig. 54) is a small room, 10 feet wide, built between two classrooms. It may be separated from these classrooms by glass partitions so that students working in the laboratory may be seen by the teacher in the adjacent room. Appropriate equipment might include a workbench with tools in one location, a flat table with drawing instruments in another. There should be shelving for books. Chairs and plenty of storage space for equipment and materials would also be required.

In some schools the mathematics laboratory is a room comparable in size to a conventional classroom in which group instruction is supplemented by individual activity requiring special equipment. In schools whose mathematics curriculum includes instruction in probability, statistics, and elementary numerical analysis, the laboratory may be a room in which students can become acquainted with the important field of digital computation and can learn to operate desk calculators by using them to solve problems that would be much too complicated to solve by pencil and paper calculations. With a relatively small financial outlay, a school can initially equip a laboratory with a set of hand-operated calculators like the Monroe Educator, which are light to carry and do not require electrical outlets. However, in planning a new laboratory for desk calculators, the possibility of changing later to electrical calculators should not be overlooked. The most important features of a laboratory for desk calculators are good lighting, good acoustics, and sturdy work tables at least 24 inches wide, equipped with a sufficient number of electrical outlets for plugging in the calculators (Fig. 25). However, such a room should also have both a chalkboard on one wall, where an instructor may explain problems, and some bulletin board space where general instructions concerning the calculators may be posted.

In the Bronx High School, New York City, and possibly others, the mathematics laboratory is equipped not only with a number of desk calculators but also with a high-speed electronic digital computer, and instruction in high-speed digital computation is available to the advanced students.

Library, seminar, and individual study rooms

The day when students learned all their mathematics from a single required textbook per year has already passed at many high schools. Increasingly, students are being encouraged to do outside reading to supplement their classroom instruction. Increasingly, high school mathematics teachers are asking for mathematical books and journals which will enrich the regular course of study and will stimulate their students to creative activities of their own.

THE AVAILABILITY OF BOOKS Related to the provision of an adequate mathematics library facility in a high school are two important questions: what books to get and where to put them. Assistance in the first problem has recently been given by the high school and junior college mathematics honor society, Mu Alpha Theta, which has compiled a list of recommended mathematics books and journals for high schools and has made available certain book collections to some of its more than 700 chapters in the form of a traveling library. Other lists are also available.

At some schools, the problem of where to keep the mathematics books is no problem. They are all in the school library and may not be taken out. In other schools, it is considered highly desirable for students to take library books home. However, before taking out a book the student must have the desire to read it. In this, he can be greatly helped by a good teacher who knows the book and recommends it. First, then, someone in the school must become aware of appropriate mathematics books, convince the authorities that these books are desirable so that money is made available, and see that they are ordered. Secondly, the attention of the mathematics teaching staff must be drawn to these books, which might be suitable for their classes or useful for their own edification. Thirdly, the teachers must make a positive effort to bring good books to the attention of their students.

One scheme to make sure that all the mathematics teachers have the opportunity to become aware of new books and journals in their field would be to display these books and journals, for a period of possibly two weeks after they are catalogued, on special shelves in the mathematics department headquarters or teachers' room. A device to assist teachers in bringing books to the attention of their students would be to provide small book collections in each mathematics laboratory or classroom, or to arrange to have a book cart with a collection of books, which could be rolled into one classroom for a few days and then moved down to another. Whatever the mechanical arrangements that are adopted at a particular school, the objective should be to make as many as possible of the mathematics students both aware of good books and desirous of reading them. Appropriate arrangements for displaying books and journals should be considered in the design of high school classrooms for mathematics and in the design of office space for teachers.

SEMINAR ROOMS There are a number of activities in a high school for which a room seating 10 or 15 people, and equipped with chalk-board on at least one wall, would be ideal (Fig. 53). Teachers who work together in team teaching need a suitable seminar room in which they can talk over their plans without disturbing others. Teachers who are trying to increase their competence in certain areas of mathematics may find it helpful to convene in small groups to discuss the materials. Groups of students who have been learning mathematics in large groups or by television may wish to get together to exchange questions and work on problems. Occasionally, a small group of enterprising students may wish to prepare themselves for advanced placement examinations on subjects not regularly taught in school. Students might do make-up work in such a room using programed instruction. Others may wish to assemble in small groups to prepare a talk for the mathematics club. These are a few of the activities that might take place in a high school if an appropriate seminar room were available.

INDIVIDUAL STUDY SPACE One of the important disadvantages of large-room instruction, either by means of large lectures or television, is a reduction in the amount of individual participation in the learning process. To counterbalance this, many teachers feel that students should have more time as well as suitable space for individual study. In some schools, this individual study will be centered primarily in the library, where provision must be made for an adequate number of individual student stations designed for reading and writing. In other situations, the use of small seminar rooms or private cubicles might be fitting.

Some schools are already taking an active interest in various types of programed learning. If this is to become a significant element in the instructional pattern, appropriate student stations must be provided (see p. 149).

Offices for the teaching faculty and departmental administration

Any teacher will do a better teaching job if he has a desk and study area of his own than if he is forced to organize his class presentations in a teachers' room of inadequate size or in a crowded corridor between classes. Ideally, each teacher in a high school should have an office of his own, either close to or opening into a departmental office in which the teachers will share common facilities. A departmental center of 1,000 square feet for a department of six mathematics teachers might contain six individual offices of 100 square feet each and a common area of 400 square feet including the following facilities: a desk and work area for a departmental secretary, a conference table for six with adjacent chalk-board (Fig. 55), a work area for duplicating machines and typewriters, a refreshment corner with coffee-making facilities, adequate shelving for books and journals, and storage for supplies and equipment. The secretary should be able to answer the telephone and transfer calls to the individual offices by a buzzer system.

When considerably less space is available, it may still be possible to provide privacy for individual teachers, as well as a common area for three or more. A suggestion for one way to do this is provided by a slight modification of the accommodations for graduate assistants at the University of Oklahoma. A room 16 feet wide

FIGURE 55 *Mathematics teachers' room, surrounded by six individual offices, St. Mark's School, Dallas, Texas*

and 22 feet from corridor to window could be partitioned as follows: next to the window would be a departmental area 7′ x 16′, including a 2′6″ x 5′ conference table in one end, and a lounging area in the other. The walls of this area would have two panels of chalkboard and a section of bulletin board. A narrow 5-foot passageway with three small offices on each side would connect this area to the main corridor. Above the passageway would be an air-conditioning duct serving the small offices and conference and lounging areas. Each small private office, slightly over 5 feet square, would contain two chairs (for the teacher and one visitor) and would have a desk surface 2 feet wide against the main wall, illuminated by fluorescent lights recessed under a three-shelf, built-in bookcase. Drawers would be provided under the writing surface. Acoustic tile would line the walls and ceiling. Each office would have a panel of chalkboard on one wall. Walls between the small offices would extend only up to the height of the air-conditioning duct covering the passageway, in order to allow for the circulation of air above. One or more telephones would be provided to serve this group of offices. The teachers' office space just described would be less than the ideal and would lack a number of desirable features, such as secretarial space, space for duplicating, storage, and the preparation of materials, and adequate space for the departmental chairman. These would have to be provided elsewhere. A variation of this arrangement is shown in Figure 56.

One way to convert a 30′ x 24′ classroom into a small teachers' room for a department chairman, a secretary or clerical aide, and five teachers, would be to partition off a 7-foot strip on the 24′ east wall opposite the door, divided into a 7′ x 9′ conference room on the northeast corner, a 7′ x 8′ cubicle for the chairman in the center, and 7′ x 7′ space for the secretary or aide in the southwest corner. The remaining 23′ along the north wall would be divided into five teacher stations wide enough for each to contain a 4-drawer letter file 15″ wide on the left and a 3-foot square desk with one bank of drawers on the right. Above each desk would be three shelves, and under the bottom shelf a shaded fluorescent light. Along the remaining 23′ of south wall, starting at the secretary's office, would be three letter files and a 12′-long work table 30″ deep, suitable for a desk calculator, materials preparation, and duplicating equipment. Beyond this, a small sink or basin, and a 6′ x 2′6″ closet with sliding doors for coats and equipment, opening next to the main door on the west wall. The 12′ wall space north of the main door on the west wall would be divided into three 4-foot strips, in each of which a pair of vertical metal strips on the wall would permit the hanging of 4-foot panels of bulletin board or chalkboard, or of shelving. Facing this wall would be a comfortable sofa, in the center of the room a 6′ x 3′ table, and on the east end, by the chairman's office, some additional shelving for books or journals (Fig. 57).

The chairman of a high school mathematics de-

FIGURE 56 *Small individual offices*

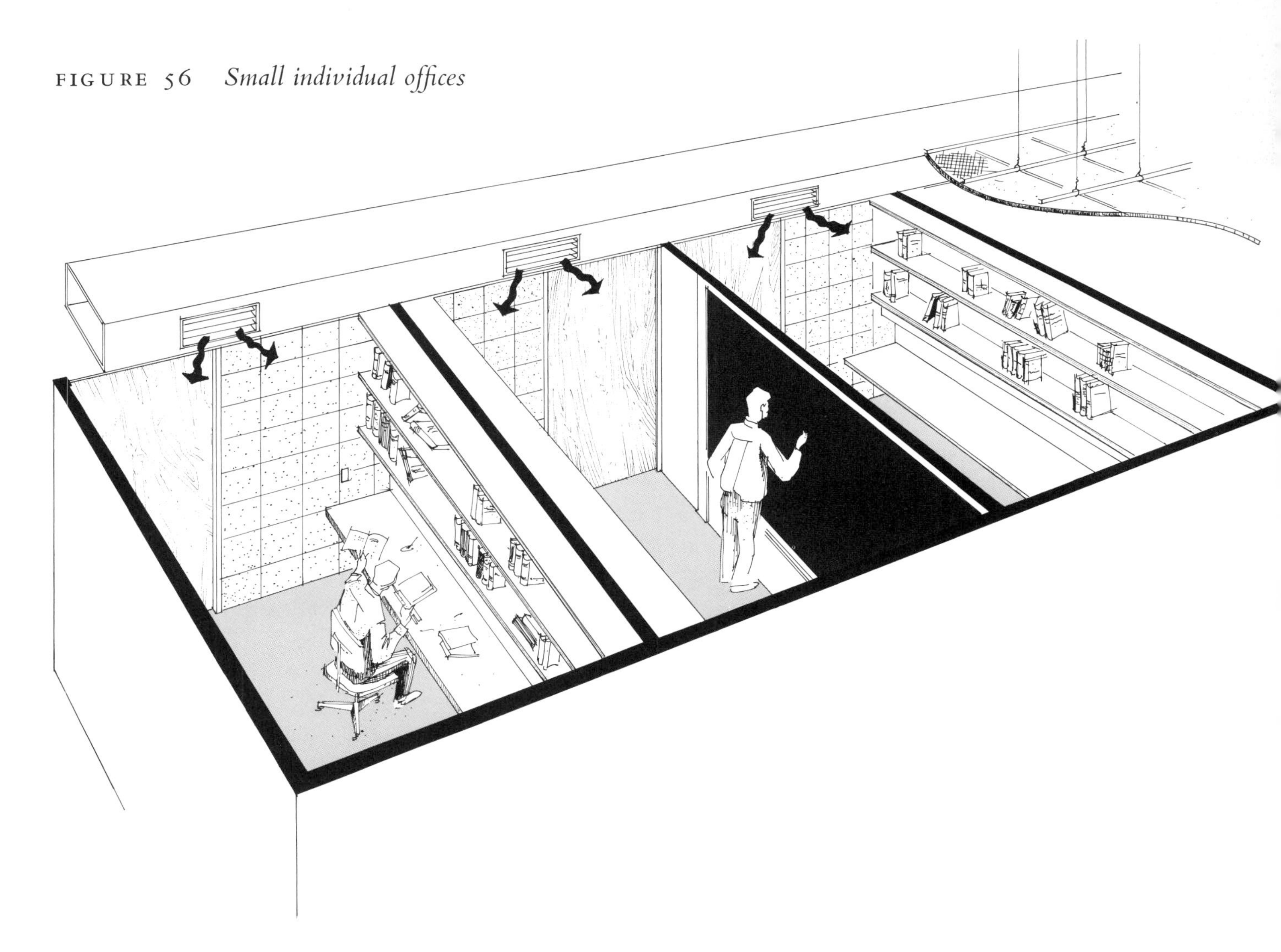

partment of more than three or four teachers should have a private office with adequate space for a desk, three or four chairs, bookshelves, and a panel of chalkboard. Adjoining his office should be space for the department's secretary or clerical aide, and adequate space for departmental files and for departmental service areas, which we will now describe.

Spaces for duplicating and preparation of materials

Every mathematics teacher in high school should have access to facilities for duplicating instructional materials, such as tests or work assignments, notes, book lists, and other written materials to be distributed to his class. Facilities should also be provided for the preparation of films or transparencies to be used in classroom instruction. In some schools, such a facility is provided in a central location for the whole school. If the mathematics department is a large one, it should have its own duplicating machine in the departmental headquarters, where teachers (preferably with the assistance of a departmental aide or secretary) could copy short items on the spur of the moment, or could leave longer manuscripts to be duplicated and overhead transparencies to be produced by departmental aides.

Many different types of duplicating equipment are available commercially, varying in price, ease of operation and correction of errors, and perfection and permanence of copy. Spirit duplicators afford ease of operation and correcting copy, and will reproduce line drawings in several colors; but they are limited to 100 or 200 copies per stencil and produce copies that may fade, if left in sunlight for an extended period. Other processes, such as mimeograph, multilith, and Xerox, are more expensive but, produce a correspondingly better copy. Machines, such as Thermofax and Ozalid, are convenient for reproducing single or multiple copies of letters, text material, current material from periodicals, or memorandums, without the need for typing them on special stencils. One possibility would be to supply each department with an inexpensive duplicating machine and to make other more expensive duplicating equipment available to the whole school in a central workroom. A decision on the location of duplicating equipment might be made as follows: if members of one department will use it frequently each day, it should be available in departmental headquarters; if it is likely not to be used more than once a day by a given department, it should probably be kept in a central school facility. Since the hands are easily soiled in using

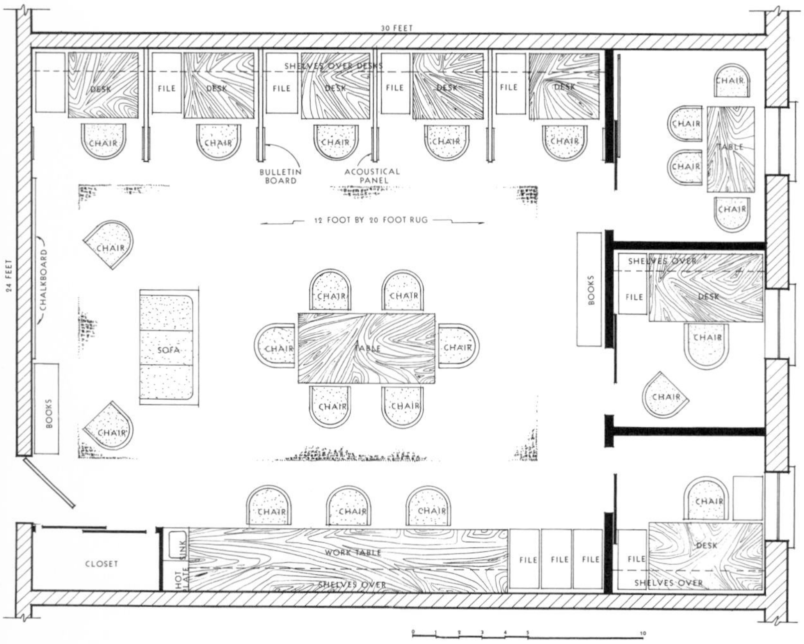

FIGURE 57 *Office space for secondary school mathematics teachers, arranged in converted classroom*

FIGURE 58 *Mathematics classroom, University High School, University of Minnesota*

certain types of duplicating equipment, it is important to have a basin with running water nearby.

Storage space

Many varieties of storage spaces are needed for a high school mathematics department. Some space should be provided in the classrooms, some in teachers' offices, some in a departmental headquarters, and possibly additional space in separate closets. In the University High School in Minneapolis (Fig. 58), the back wall of the mathematics classroom is lined with storage drawers, including nine banks of 12 drawers each for individual students, and several banks of larger drawers for class materials, including some large flat drawers for charts. Other schools provide a teachers' storage area, possibly 2 feet deep, 3 or 4 feet wide, and 6 to 8 feet high, closed by a single door, in which there is a space 1 foot wide for hanging coats, and the remainder of the space is divided into several drawers below and several shelves above. The drawers can be portable, readily transferable to the classroom. Open storage shelves may also be needed for mathematical models and other materials used in class work. If an overhead projector is to be used in class, there should should be closet space where it can be kept safely. Most teachers need space in addition to their desk drawers for keeping private instructional materials. The department office will also need plenty of storage space for its files and records and for general instructional materials that are shared by two or more teachers. Note that storage space for field work instruments, such as target poles, requires extra height.

If visual aids are to be used in classroom instruction, there must be proper storage space for the equipment itself and also for the auxiliary materials. Storage space should also be available for a variety of types of materials such as the following:

- Office supplies: chalk, stencils, paper, etc.
- Student records, worksheets, and tests
- Texts, programed texts, pamphlets, workbooks, charts
- Books for professional study or enrichment; experimental curricula
- Models and instruments
- Tools and construction materials

Visual aids and television

Visual aids for teaching mathematics,[4] much more frequently used than even a few years ago, are likely to become a major item of concern in designing and equipping a mathematics facility in the school of the future (see p.p. 137-149).[15,36] Some visual aids can be used with little or no addition to or alteration of the standard classroom. Others require built-in electrical outlets in floors or walls, conduits, wall or ceiling fixtures, shades or drapes for darkening a room, or a projection booth. Some visual aids are quite inexpensive. Others were formerly outside the range of mathematics department budgets in most schools, until the Federal Government, under Title VII of the National Defense Education Act, offered to pay a substantial part of the cost of approved equipment for teaching science and mathematics in secondary schools.

PROJECTION EQUIPMENT The overhead projector (see p. 141) is a popular visual aid both for a large lecture room and for an ordinary classroom. Using it, the teacher can write his class notes while facing the class and can also present materials, such as theorems, formulas, and carefully drawn graphs, prepared in advance on single transparencies or overlays either by the teacher himself or commercially. In classrooms, the screen for an overhead projector is commonly hung in front over the chalkboard (Figs. 50, 64). However, with this arrangement the teacher may block the view of the screen for some of the class, and the screen certainly blocks the concurrent use of a substantial portion of the front chalkboard. Hence, the teacher who wishes to combine the chalkboard and overhead projector in presenting materials might prefer to have the screen mounted in a front corner above the chalkboard and away from the windows, fastened so that it can be rolled up when not in use (Fig. 63). The screen can be suspended satisfactorily and inexpensively from two chains fastened to the ceiling and can be hooked below to the chalkboard trim or wall. For best results, the height and tilt of the screen should be figured carefully to minimize distortion (see p. 144). A suitable cabinet for the projector will be described in Part IV (p. 142).

FLIMS AND TELEVISION A number of filmstrips, films, and slides have been prepared on topics appropriate for the high school. These may be used to add variety and interest to the classroom presentation. They will be discussed in greater detail in Part IV (p. 146). In certain cases such a visual aid may present a topic that cannot otherwise be taught effectively to high school students.

Television as a medium for presenting mathematical instruction has already found acceptance in a number of high schools. Some schools present complete courses in mathematics from the 7th to the 12th grade by television, supplemented by discussion meetings with the classroom teacher (see p. 246). In some city high schools suffering from a shortage of qualified mathematics teachers, a master teacher may address several classes at once for 20 minutes on television and have his presentation followed up by questions and discussions under the direction of less experienced teachers in the several classrooms. Facilities for producing and monitoring television presentations of mathematics classes will be discussed in Part IV (p.p. 147-148).

SLIDE RULE A demonstration slide rule is one of the most common visual aids found in a high school mathematics classroom. Sometimes it is hung from the map rail above the chalkboard, but in this position it may interfere with the use of the chalkboard and not be easily manipulated. Some shorter teachers cannot reach the map rail. A better arrangement is to hang the slide rule from the ceiling about 3 feet in front of the chalkboard, using a counterbalanced pulley system, so that the rule may be pushed up near the ceiling when not in use and yet be easily pulled down in front of the teacher for demonstrations. If two sides of the slide rule are to be used, the mounting should permit its rotation about a horizontal axis. Needless to say, the slide rule should be mounted far enough from the side walls so that the slider can be pulled to its full length on either side. An alternative to the large demonstration slide rule is a small transparent one whose scales can be projected onto a screen by an overhead projector.

AIDS IN GRAPHING The graphing of points and lines may be made more vivid by using small magnets, on a panel of steel chalkboard, to represent points and colored elastic strings attached to magnets to represent lines. Points and lines may also be plotted quickly by using pegs and elastic thread on a panel of pegboard. Pegboards can be used to support displays of models or books, or shelving for a variety of visual aids.

The trimetric ruler is a visual aid in the form of a triangle with different uniform scales marked on its three edges, representing, in magnitude and direction, the projections of equal subdivisions on three mutually perpendicular lines in space. It assists the teacher and students in making three-dimensional line drawings, on a chalkboard or sheet of paper, as they would look if projected perpendicularly from space onto the drawing plane.[23]

More elaborate drawing equipment for the chalkboard is also available, including equipment to facilitate the drawing of parallel lines, and even computer-driven equipment to plot curves. A simple device for drawing parallel lines is a meter stick or yardstick about 3 inches wide in which four small congruent rollers are inserted in slots, one near each of the four corners. Each roller, mounted on a pin or axle parallel to the long edges of the stick, has a diameter slightly greater than the width of the stick. Thus, when the device is placed against the chalkboard, it can be moved parallel to itself on these rollers.

The total environment

Mathematics classrooms, laboratories, and offices should not only contain the requisite equipment for the mathematical activities to be served, but these places where teachers and students work should also be pleasant, comfortable, and well planned. Factors of beauty and light, sound and comfort, which contribute to this attractiveness of the total environment have been discussed in Chapter 3 (p. 46). They certainly play an important role in the design of high school facilities.

The right use of color, both in the chairs and fixed furnishings, can contribute to making the various learning spaces attractive. Because the study of mathematics is important, it should not necessarily be dull or unpleasant. A pleasant environment can contribute to the well-being of both the teacher and the class.

Good lighting in all the work areas is most important. In general, it is better to illuminate a room by lighted strips or areas in the ceiling than by point sources of light. A strip of light to illuminate a chalkboard should be mounted away from the front wall, either in the ceiling or on a special support, where it is shielded from the eyes of the class. If an overhead projector is to be used in a room with high illumination, it is advantageous to provide the lecturer with a switch for dimming the lights to a point where the students can easily see both the projected image and their own writing surface, or by providing separate controls for the lights over the screen and those over the students' writing surfaces.

Requirements for heating and air conditioning may vary in different parts of the country, but as schools are used increasingly during the summer months, air conditioning may become a necessity in places where it was once considered a luxury. The problem of the noise developed by an air-conditioning system must not be overlooked. In some cases it is so distracting to the speaker and to his audience that both prefer to suffer the heat rather than the noise.

Good acoustics are a most important attribute of a good classroom. Two types of acoustical problems must be solved: one concerns the transmission of sound between rooms, and the other concerns the reflection and absorption of sound within the room. Undesirable sound transmission may occur between rooms, either through the walls themselves or through the heating and air-conditioning ducts or through spaces above the ceilings. Noise through the ducts may be reduced by lining them with sound-absorbent materials. In planning a school building, one should avoid placing noisy areas next to instructional areas, where such noise would be a distraction. Within the room itself, new techniques in acoustical design can contribute greatly to a pleasant environment. Acoustical tile and pegboards serve as sound absorbers. In one experimental classroom, the acoustic tile is hung from the ceiling in strips 1 foot high and about 30 inches apart, with fluorescent lights mounted half-way between the acoustic strips (Fig. 58). Strips of tile serve both to trap the sound and to shield the eyes from the direct glare of the light.

Wall-to-wall carpeting has been tried in some schools[45] to improve the environment in both classrooms and offices (Fig. 55). At first sight, such carpeting seems to be a luxury that only the most wealthy schools could afford. However, recent controlled experiments have indicated (possibly without sufficient evidence to be conclusive) that, under certain circumstances, the use of carpeting involves savings which recover the initial extra cost of the carpeting in a 10-year period. It was found that carpeting was cheaper to clean and maintain than the usual tile floor, that it saved on heat bills by insulating the floor, and that it saved on the cost of acoustical treatment for the ceiling and walls, since the carpet itself was the most effective absorber of noise. Teachers in carpeted schools were enthusiastic and felt that the carpets contributed to the better behavior of the students.

The implications of flexibility

It is generally accepted that flexibility is an important feature in the design of a building, but flexibility means many things,[35] and certain types of flexibility may not be worth the cost involved. What is needed is not complete, but selective flexibility. Certain types of flexibility are concerned with the multiple use of spaces in the same day; for example, a cafetorium or even a wide hallway might be used for cafeteria tables during the noon hour and as an assembly area at some other time. Another type of flexibility is long range; for example, a classroom or seminar room might be placed next to the library in such a way that it could be converted into library space when such expansion becomes necessary (Fig. 7a). A classroom not initially intended for television reception might nevertheless be planned with appropriate conduits, so that it could be converted to television use at a later date.

Some of the types of flexibility that are of

greatest concern for a mathematics department are those involving operable partitions between rooms (see p. 71),[19,45] those involving mobility of chalkboards and other furniture within a classroom (see p. 139), and those that make provision for future growth or for new techniques of instruction (see p. 16).

The use of folding partitions to separate a large classroom into two smaller rooms has been discussed in connection with team teaching (p. 118). It also is illustrated in the plans for a mathematics facility for a large university (Figure 10b), where a 40′ x 30′ classroom for 60 students is divided into two 20′ x 30′ rooms for 30 students each. If one of the 40-foot walls is taken as the front wall, 9 feet could be left between the chalkboard and the first row of seats, and six rows of 10 seats each could be spaced 3 feet apart on center and still allow slightly over 3 feet for a back aisle. Down the center might be a 3-foot aisle with a central track along which the folding partition could be pulled from back to front. There could be a 3-foot aisle along each side wall. Each half of the room might contain five seats 22 inches wide in each of six rows, with a spacing of 41 inches between seat centers in a row ($36'' + 11'' + 4 \times 41'' + 11'' + 18'' = 240''$). Or, instead of six rows of five seats in each half room, there could be five rows of three $18'' \times 48''$ tables with two chairs each, spaced 45 inches between seat centers from back to front, with 24-inch aisles between tables ($36'' + 3 \times 48'' + 2 \times 24'' + 12'' = 240''$). A slightly larger room $42' \times 30'$ would allow 3′6″ aisles at the sides and a 4′ aisle at the center.

It is important that the folding partition be of such quality that it will reduce the sound transmission between the rooms to acceptable levels (p. 72). Poor acoustic insulation is a source of irritation to both teachers and students. Effective sound reduction can be achieved, however, if the folding partition is made up of three layers, with heavy sound-absorbent material in the middle, and if the partition when closed makes a tight seal with the floor and ceiling and also along the vertical strips where it joins the wall or another partition.

The mounting of chalkboards is another place where flexibility may be desirable. In each case it is necessary to balance the cost against the advantages to be achieved. Large panels of vertically sliding chalkboard will be very welcome to most mathematics teachers. However, there are some devotees of the overhead projector for whom such a facility would be an unjustifiable expense. Vertically sliding chalkboards mounted on rolling standards are available in this country but are naturally more expensive than a fixed board (see p. 139). They could, however, serve a dual purpose as a writing surface and as a space divider for occasionally separating off a small area of the classroom for individual study. Hinged panels of chalkboard might serve a similar purpose.

A panel of pegboard on the wall affords flexible use, either to support bookshelves, to display models, or to serve as a sound-absorbing surface to improve the acoustics. A map rail along the top of the chalkboard provides flexibility for a variety of uses. Similarly, a narrow 2-inch strip of tackboard above the chalkboard permits charts and drawings to be tacked up for temporary display.

Since a school building may be built to last for 50 years or more, some thought must be given to changing conditions implied either by growth or by changing techniques of instruction.[13] Flexibility may be required to adapt the classrooms to instruction by television or to instruction by teaching machines. Considerably more space may be needed for individual study stations (see p. 125). If the high school becomes truly flexible, so that every pupil is not in class every hour, some study areas and individual study stations will be essential.

ABOVE *A modern classroom with overhead projector.*
RIGHT *A Power projector in use around 1922.*

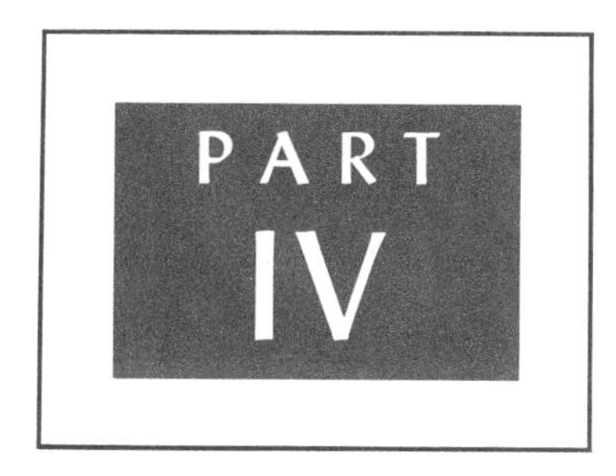

INSTRUCTIONAL MATERIALS FOR COLLEGES AND SECONDARY SCHOOLS

Part Four is concerned with some of the important equipment and facilities for mathematical instruction in colleges and secondary schools; these include chalkboards, overhead projectors, facilities for rear-screen projection, films, television, models and other visual aids, and programed instructional materials.

11 INSTRUCTIONAL MATERIALS FOR COLLEGES AND SECONDARY SCHOOLS

Chalkboards and chalk

The chalkboard has been and still is one of the most useful visual aids in the classroom teaching of mathematics. It is also used by mathematicians in their offices for exchanging ideas with students and colleagues and for private research. One should not be surprised on entering a mathematician's office to find him contemplating a chalkboard (Fig. 30) full of mathematical symbols, theorems, equations, or graphs, which he is studying intently and modifying when a new idea emerges. Flow diagrams for a computer may take shape on a chalkboard before being written on paper. Mathematicians talking shop in a restaurant are sometimes frustrated by the lack of a chalkboard, and they may even be so inconsiderate as to write on the table top or on a menu or napkin. A mathematician may communicate with one other mathematician on paper, despite the annoyance of erasing; but when he talks shop to more than one other person, he usually wants a chalkboard.

MATERIALS AND COLORS Many different materials and colors are now used in the manufacture of chalkboards.[2] In fact, the availability of boards in a variety of colors—green, blue, white, tan, as well as grey-black—led to changing the older name "blackboard" to "chalkboard." The traditional and still very popular slate now competes with such materials as porcelain steel, glass, and several so-called composition materials, including cement asbestos, formica, linoleum, silicon carbide, and other patented synthetic products. Although most mathematicians who express themselves about chalkboards seem to prefer slate[5] (and slate was used in the new mathematics buildings at the University of Wisconsin and Dartmouth), some have had good experience with one or more of the other materials and recommend them. Steel has advantages for visual aids using magnets (see p. 131). Painted wood is used extensively in Europe. In the United States, experiments have also been made with large floor-to-ceiling wall panels that double as a writing surface, and with a chalkboard surface painted directly on plaster. Some major factors influencing the choice of a chalkboard are: 1) color, light reflectance, and contrast; 2) ease of writing, erasing, and maintenance; 3) cost and durability; and 4) weight and mobility.

To the casual observer, the most obvious difference between chalkboards is their color. Related somewhat to the color is the light reflectance which may range from 10 per cent on blue-black board to 20 per cent on a light green board, under "in use" conditions. Involved in the choice of colors, both for the chalkboard and the chalk used on it, are factors of contrast for ready visibility and the avoidance of eye strain from prolonged viewing. Slateboard manufacturers point out that color-blind students may have difficulty in distinguishing colored chalk against a colored board.

LIGHT REFLECTANCE AND LIGHTING OF CHALKBOARDS The American Standard Guide for School Lighting (1962)[1] makes the following recommendations concerning chalkboards (Fig. 59):

"Chalkboards should meet two brightness standards. They should be light enough to blend well with the background, and dark enough to provide sufficient contrast to chalk writing. A chalkboard should be measured for reflectance number 'in use' conditions, with a typical amount of chalk film on its surface. Colored boards should not exceed 20 per cent reflectance under these conditions. Black chalkboards in use are not usually black, but dark grey, with 5 to 10 per cent reflectance.

"In elementary schools, a student may be 30 feet away from a chalkboard. In college, he may be further than 50 feet away. For this reason the writing on the board should give a good chalk contrast. This may be achieved with the help of supplementary lighting. This extra lighting can be used as well to improve the brightness ratio between the board and its surrounding surfaces."

The use of supplementary lighting for chalkboards is desirable for all chalkboards in mathematics classrooms. It is mandatory in large lecture rooms.

MAINTENANCE AND PERFORMANCE From the teacher's point of view, the best chalkboard is the one that is easiest to write on and easiest to erase; from the custodian's point of view, the best chalkboard is the one that is easiest to clean. Many teachers and custodians may not know that the performance of a board depends not only on the material of which it is made, but on the way it is maintained. For example, when certain boards are wiped off with a damp sponge they become covered with a thin film of material from the binder in the chalk, which causes the writing surface to become glazed. Such boards must be washed thoroughly or not at all. Some boards are damaged by water and cannot be washed. Even assuming proper maintenance, some boards present a much better writing surface than others.

FIGURE 59 *Illumination of chalkboards*

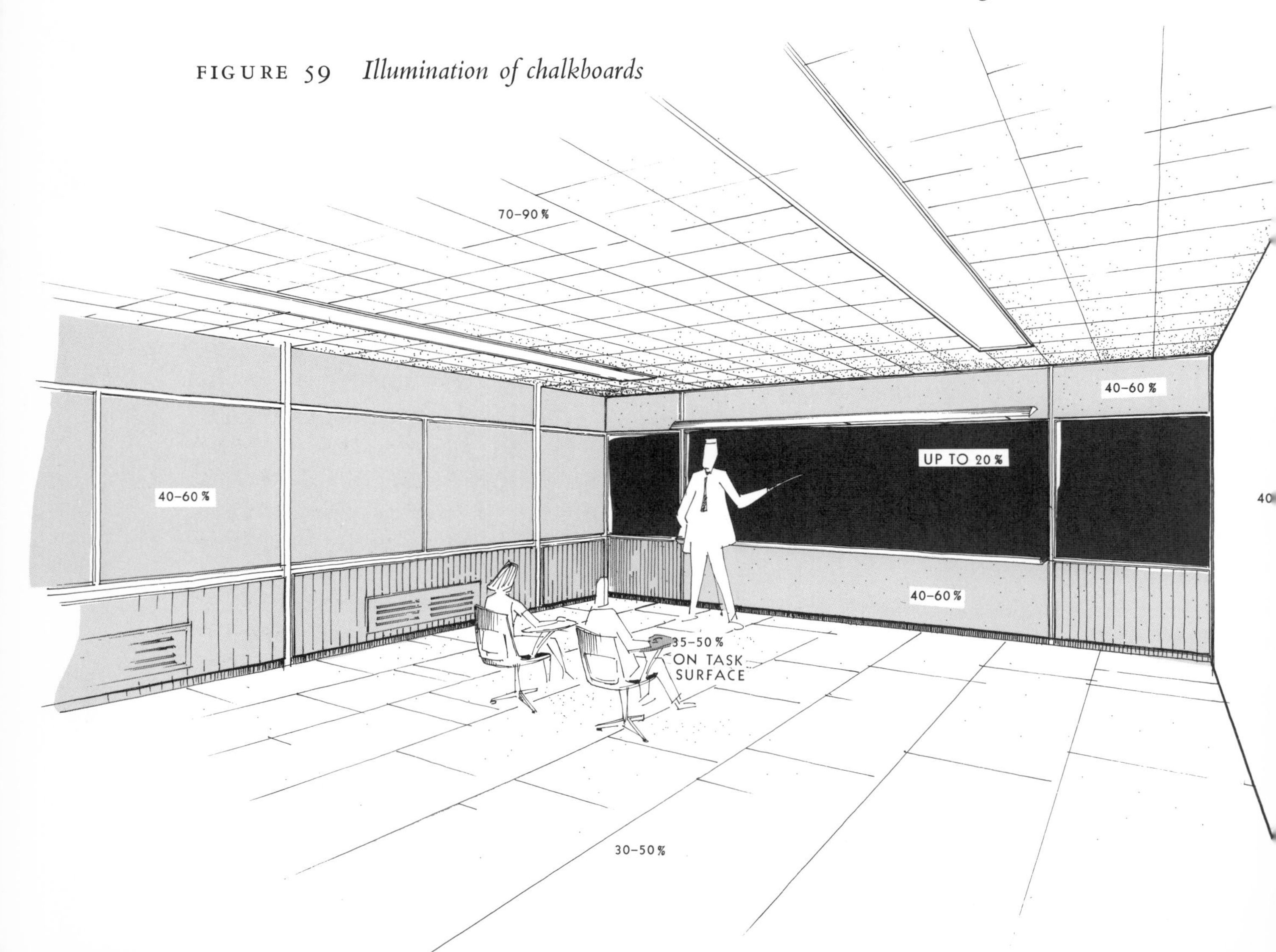

CHALK AND CHALKHOLDERS Good quality chalk is also important—not too dusty, too gritty, too soft, or too hard. Certain types of art chalk that are not intended for chalkboard use can damage a chalkboard and make it difficult to write on. Certain boards require special types of chalk. Chalkholders for white and colored chalk can be used to reduce the soiling of hands and clothes by chalk-dust.

COST While cost is a factor in deciding on the choice of chalkboard, it is not the initial cost only that should be considered but rather the sum of the initial cost, maintenance cost, repair cost, and replacement cost over a period of years. Some boards with a higher initial cost per square foot may actually save money in the long run because they are cheaper to maintain and may last 100 years instead of only 10. An initially cheap board is not really inexpensive if it buckles or warps or loses its good writing surface within a few years and has to be replaced. Some materials contract and expand more than others when a building is cooled over the week-end and re-heated Monday morning. Such thermal stresses are one cause for warping. The initial cost of a chalkboard includes materials costs, transportation costs, and installation costs. Materials costs will vary considerably, depending on the materials, and may be as low as 60 cents per square foot or as high as $2. Experience has testified to the durability of slate and its excellence as a writing surface.[5]

MOUNTINGS Weight and mobility become a factor in the choice of chalkboard when the board is not to be mounted permanently in one position on a wall. Chalkboards that are not completely immovable may vary considerably in their mobility. One type of mounting provides vertical strips fastened permanently to the wall, but is arranged so that the chalkboard may be fastened at different heights to the same mounting. Thus, for example, a 9th grade class might use the room one term and a 12th grade class might use the room later with the chalkboards raised a few inches. Still more flexible are chalkboards, either fixed to the wall or on rolling standards, that are so mounted and counterbalanced as to be easily raised and lowered by the writer. Those on sturdy, movable stands, which may be rolled from place to place and also moved vertically, are well known in parts of Europe; they are available, but not often used in the United States (Fig. 60).

A highly satisfactory arrangement of chalkboards for the front wall of a mathematics classroom or lecture room is provided by mounting several panels of board, each balanced by counterweights, so that they hang between vertical tracks and can be raised and lowered without difficulty. The use of roller bearings at one institution and of teflon at another has been effective in reducing friction. At one time, the heaviness of slate was a deterrent to its use as an operable board, but this disadvantage has been overcome by well-balanced counterweights and proper mounting. If chalkboard panels less than 6 feet wide are used, it may be desirable to divide the writing space on the front wall into three sections (Fig. 23) and to mount two or three boards in each section, one of which may be a fixed board. For better visibility, it may be desirable to mount the outer tracks slightly away from the wall, so that the planes of the outer panels make angles of slightly less than 180° with the planes of the center panels. A board mounted on roller bearings may vibrate less during use if the lower ends of the vertical tracks are a few inches further away from the wall than the upper ends.

Many mathematicians feel that a well counterbalanced, properly mounted, hand-operated system of boards is superior to a motor-driven one; however, if boards more than 10 feet wide are used, a motor drive may be necessary (Fig. 15). Controls for moving the board should be easy to locate and easy to operate. There should be an automatic shutoff to prevent a board from moving too high or too low.

Partial mobility is also obtained by mounting panels of chalkboard on horizontal tracks. In some cases, fixed chalkboard panels painted with grids for polar coordinates or rectangular coordinates may be temporarily covered by plain panels sliding on a horizontal track. A variety of panels of chalkboard, bulletin board, or pegboard might be stored on separate tracks in a common container at one side of the front wall; these panels could be selected at will by a switching device. An advantage of horizontal over vertical mobility is that a map rail can be installed permanently above the chalkboard, from which maps or charts, screens, demonstration slide rules, and other heavy classroom accessories can be hung. In addition, lighter display materials can be fastened on a thin strip of tackboard above the map rail.

One major trouble with chalkboards that roll or slide on a horizontal track at the bottom is that chalk very easily gets crushed in the tracks and may lock the board or make it difficult to move. A board that hangs on rollers from an overhead track avoids this difficulty.

Two great advantages of a vertically sliding chalkboard over a horizontally sliding board are visibility and ease of writing. The lecturer writes at a height convenient to him and pushes the board up when he writes the next line. If someone in the back of the room cannot see a line when it is written, he may be able to see it later. On the other hand, when a short teacher writes on a horizontally sliding board in a large room, he may be

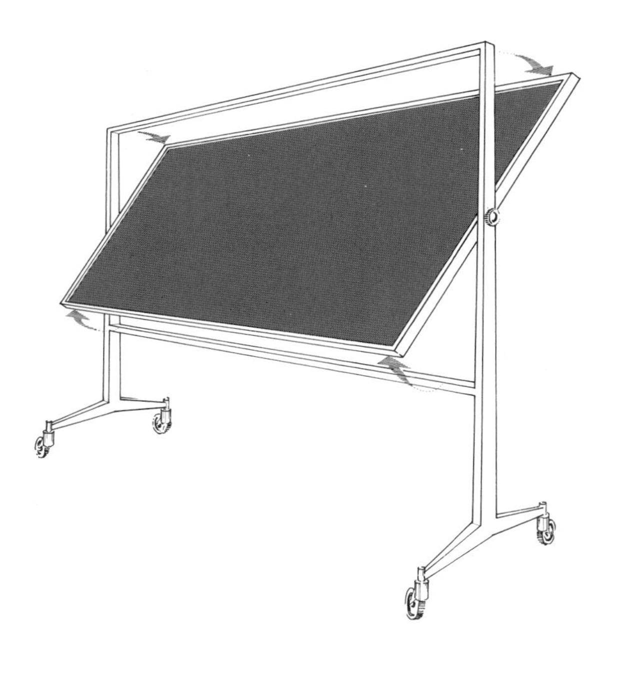

FIGURE 60 *Portable chalkboards*

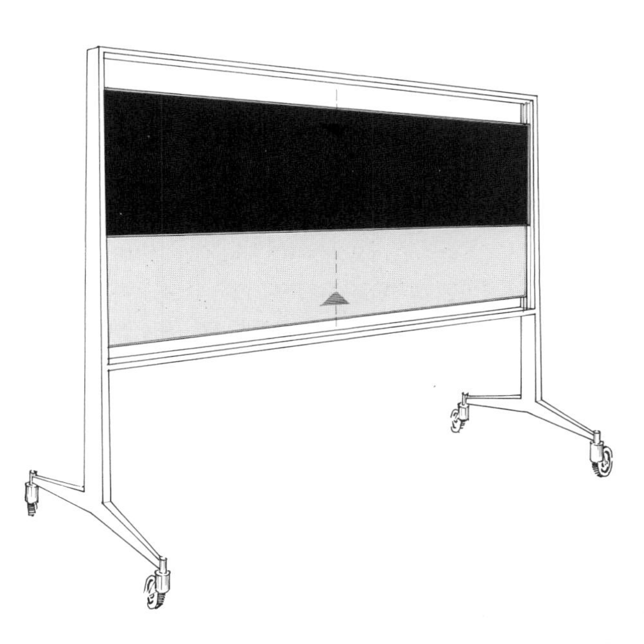

limited to a few lines per panel, since he cannot reach the upper part of the board, and the lower part cannot be seen beyond the first four rows of seats.

AMOUNT OF CHALKBOARD REQUIRED Most mathematics teachers are content only with a large amount of available chalkboard surface. Some insist that chalkboard should be mounted on at least three sides of the classroom so that students may work problems at the board (pp. 119–120). At the U.S. Air Force Academy, mathematics classrooms for 16 to 18 students are interior rooms with chalkboard on all four walls (Fig. 52). Some teachers, especially in the large lecture rooms, want all the board space at the front, but would like, if possible, to be able to write the salient points in a 50-minute lecture without erasing. This might be possible if each of three sections of vertical track carried three large panels.

When a mathematics teacher, who wants lots of chalkboard surface, has to share a classroom with a teacher in another discipline, who requires more wall space devoted to bulletin boards, consideration should be given to dual-purpose panels that can be turned to display chalkboard on the one side or bulletin board on the other.

COORDINATE GRIDS Grids for rectangular and polar coordinates are desirable for a mathematics classroom and can be made available to the mathematics teacher in a number of ways. They may be provided ready-made on two sides of a slated cloth that is hung from the map rail when in use and rolled up for storage; or they may be dusted on quickly with a chalky felt eraser through holes in a large rubberized graph chart stencil hung temporarily from several positions on the map rail, so that several gridded panels may be used by students at once. They may be provided on portable chalkboard panels. They may be permanently painted on a fixed panel of chalkboard which can be covered by a sliding plain panel; or they may be drawn on a regular chalkboard panel with a Listo pencil, which leaves a line that is not easily erased, but may be removed by glass wax. Still another possibility is to project a coordinate grid onto the chalkboard from an overhead projector. An imaginative designer might devise ways to paint a coordinate grid on a chalkboard so that it would show only when illuminated by special lights.

Overhead projectors

The overhead projector (Fig. 61) is a device for projecting onto a screen (Figs. 15, 50, 64) or white wall surface (Fig. 62) enlarged images, either of specially prepared transparencies (for permanent or temporary use) or of materials being written on a transparent sheet of plastic. A lecturer using the overhead projector faces the audience while he talks. He may present materials to the class by laying a prepared transparency on a flat glass plate illuminated from below, so that the image is projected, after reflection, onto a screen at the front of the room above and behind the lecturer's head. He may write with a special grease pencil directly on a special transparency sheet or on a roll of transparent plastic material, which he pulls over the glass writing surface to raise or lower the image. He may even display small objects, such as the scales on a transparent slide rule, and have them magnified so as to be easily visible to a large group.

Commercial overhead projectors, of which Vu-Graph, Beseler, and Transpaque are three of the many varieties, range in cost from $155 for small models to between $300 and $500 for models suitable for use in a large lecture room, and on up to thousands of dollars for certain special-purpose projectors. Those with brighter lights may be quite hot to write on unless suitably cooled. Extra cooling devices and more adjustability add to the expense.

Transparencies for use with an overhead projector can be prepared photographically from printed materials or from a written manuscript. Sequences of transparencies have been prepared by commercial companies to present whole courses. With an overhead projector, it is possible to show the consecutive steps in a construction by placing several transparencies one over the other, each adding new parts to the previous figures. The lecturer before a large class has several obvious advantages in presenting his lecture materials on the tablet of a transparent projector, instead of on the chalkboard:

1 The lecturer writes facing the class.
2 Ordinary-sized writing can be magnified so as to be seen clearly by a large audience.
3 Small objects and scales (as on a slide rule) may be enlarged so as to be visible to more than two or three students at once.
4 Graphs, formulas, tables, and other information may be prepared neatly and carefully once, and be used again for many different classes.
5 More material can be covered more effectively in less time.

FIGURE 61 *Overhead projector on movable storage cabinet*

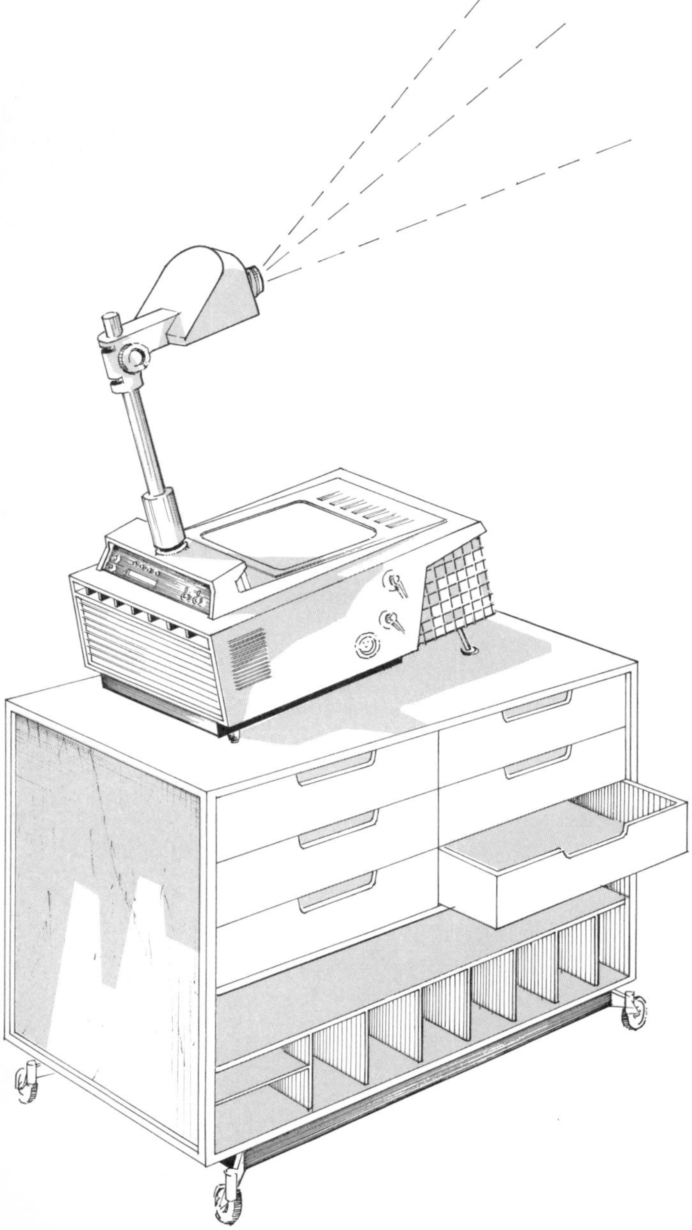

Some disadvantages of the overhead projector as compared with the chalkboard are:

1 Only a small area of written material, less than one panel of chalkboard, can be shown at one time by a single overhead projector.
2 A lecture, for which all written materials have been prepared in advance on overlays for a projector, may lack spontaneity and may also allow insufficient time for note-taking by students.
3 Mathematics teachers have had so little experience with the equipment that they may be more concerned with the mechanics than the substance of the presentation.

These disadvantages may all be overcome. The presentation area may be increased by using more than one projector and keeping some displayed materials on one screen while other screens or other portions of a single wide screen are used for developing the subject. Time needed for note-taking may be reduced by duplicating outlines and highlights of each lesson and distributing them to the students. The obvious way to overcome inexperience with the equipment is to learn to use it.

A projector should preferably be placed on a movable cabinet (Fig. 61) made for the express purpose of holding the projector on top, with an open shelf for papers, books, and overlays, either

FIGURE 62 *Student projecting homework, Fridley (Minnesota) Senior High School*

just below or hinged at one side, and with accessible closed storage space underneath for such supplies as an extra light bulb, extension cord, wax pencils, cleaner fluid, cleaning rags, disposable tissues, extra transparency sheets and mounts, and an extra roll for overhead projection. The overhead projector mounted on a movable cabinet or stand requires a suitable place for its storage. There must also be appropriate storage space for the transparencies, whether purchased or locally prepared, and suitable places for teachers to prepare their projection materials. Some schools find the overhead projector so popular that they provide one for each of their mathematics classrooms (Figs. 62, 64). Electrical outlets properly located on the floor or wall should be provided for connecting overhead projectors in any classroom in which they might be used. If the projector stand does not have adequate space for the lecturer's books, notes, and transparencies, such space should be provided nearby. If the lecturer has a long table on wheels or casters instead of a fixed table (Fig. 15), the projector can be suitably centered, and the lecturer can bring his materials to a convenient position. Pulled next to the projector, this table also serves as a seat for a tall lecturer while he is writing class notes for overhead projection. If the projector is permanently fastened on a table, provision should be made for its protection against damage.

The screen for the projector (or more than one, if needed) should be mounted in such a way that the class has a good view of the image. A screen mounted high in a front corner of a classroom will permit the lecturer to use the chalkboard and overhead projector at the same time (see Fig. 63).

FIGURE 63 *Corner mounting for overhead projector screen, Cubberley Senior High School, Palo Alto, Cal.*

If the top of a 6-foot screen is mounted 12 to 18 inches farther from the wall than the bottom is fastened (see Fig. 64),[46] the screen will make an angle of about 10 to 15 degrees with the wall, and this will avoid a pronounced distortion of the image, known as "keystoning" (Fig. 15, 62) produced when a rectangle is distorted into a trapezoid in the shape of a keystone with a wider top than base. The same screen, tilted for an overhead projector, might be hung vertically for movies projected from a great distance. Beaded screens give good reflection only near the optical axis; they are not recommended for use in a large auditorium. Here, a fixed reflecting surface of dull, white, painted hard-board is quite adequate, mounted above or behind the sliding chalkboard panels.

OPAQUE PROJECTOR The opaque projector reflects an image from a sheet of paper or the page of a book onto a screen and is used to display printed materials, such as graphs or charts, without manual or photographic copying. It can be operated either by the speaker himself or by an assistant. Since it uses reflected light, it requires more intense lighting and gives off more heat to produce a given illumination in the projected image than is required for projection through a transparency.

Projection of movies, slides, and filmstrips

The use of movies, slides, or filmstrips in mathematical instruction will require not only portable equipment, but electrical outlets and other fixtures that should be provided even for the smaller classrooms when the building is built. The large lecture room needs a complete projection system. Essentially, there are two methods of projection. One is the front-screen method in which an image is reflected off a screen mounted on or near the front wall of the lecture room. The other is the so-called rear-screen method, recently developed, in which an image is projected onto a translucent screen, mounted in the front wall of the lecture room, from a projector located in an adjacent room on the other side of the front wall (Fig. 65). To rectify the reversal of the image, it is necessary either to turn the film before projecting it or to insert a mirror between the projector and the translucent screen. Rear-screen projection has the advantage that the noise and heat emitted by the projector are not in the lecture room itself, and the equipment is not in a position to obstruct the view of the audience or to clutter the floor with cables. It has the disadvantages of requiring additional space for the projection room and of requiring projectors of higher brightness and shorter focal length. The short focal length tends to produce images that are less sharp and slightly distorted at the edges.

At the time of this writing, most of the available equipment is designed for front projection. Projectors whose ratio of projection distance to image size is six to one or more are commonly located behind the seating area, possibly in a projection booth. They may be operated by someone other than the lecturer, but may also be operated by remote control by the lecturer himself. The projector should be placed high enough so that the projection beam is entirely above the heads of the audience.

MATHEMATICAL FILMS Moving pictures have not yet been used very extensively in mathematics instruction at the college level, chiefly because few very good films are available. The Mathematical Association of America has pioneered in this field by sponsoring a film on *Theory of Limits* by Pro-

FIGURE 64 *Tilted screen for overhead projector, Newton South High School, Mass.*

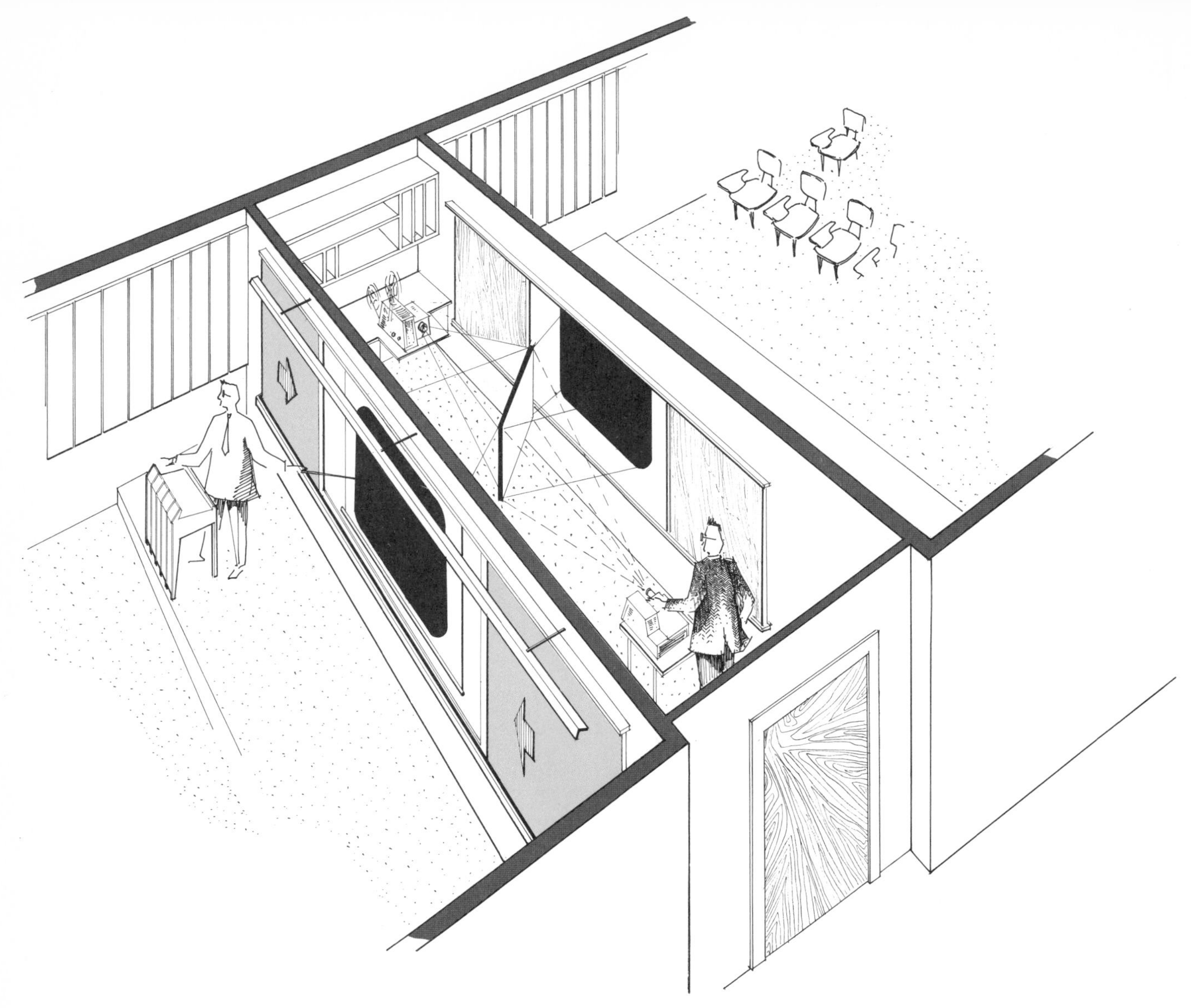

FIGURE 65 *Rear screen projection for two classrooms*

fessor E. J. McShane, one on *Mathematical Induction* by Professor Leon Henkin, one on *Integration* by Professor Edwin Hewitt, and one on *The Kakeya Problem* by Professor A. S. Besicovitch. A joint conference of the Mathematical Association of America, the National Council of Teachers of Mathematics, and the School Mathematics Study Group on mathematics films, in June 1962, has recommended the formation of a coordinating committee to stimulate the production of approved films and other audio-visual materials and to seek the establishment of a permanent Mathematics Film Center. A number of filmstrips, slides, and films have been prepared on mathematical topics appropriate for the high school. While these do not take the place of classroom instruction, they may be used to add variety and interest to the presentation. In certain cases, a visual aid may set forth a topic that cannot otherwise be effectively presented to high school students. When more mathematical films of high quality become available for widespread use, they will become an important adjunct to mathematical instruction both in schools and in universities.

Television

Since buildings and facilities for mathematics must be planned not only for the present but for the future, it is necessary to consider the implications for building design of possible future use of television in mathematics instruction.[10,37,65]

The presentation of mathematics by television was begun on a national scale in a series of broadcasts called the "Continental Classroom." Professor John L. Kelley presented a course in *Modern Algebra,* with the assistance of Dr. Julius H. Hlavaty, in the fall semester 1960–61; and Professor Frederick Mosteller presented a course in *Probability and Statistics,* with the assistance of Professor Paul C. Clifford, in the spring semester. Both courses were broadcast at 6:30 a.m. in that year and were repeated at 6 a.m. the following year. A few universities have experimented with the offering of regular college courses by closed circuit television. Others propose to offer remedial work in high school subjects, such as algebra, geometry, and trigonometry, by television only, and to start their college credit course offerings with analytic geometry and calculus. If university mathematics departments are successful in presenting one or two mathematics courses on television, they may try this technique with other courses. It should be borne in mind that the presentation of a mathematics course on television is not a saving in time or money unless large numbers of students are to be reached. The break-even point may be a class of 250 or 300 students. It is a full-time assignment for a teacher to prepare three or four one-half hour television presentations per week. However, if the group to be served numbers 500 or more, or if the same course can be shown in successive terms to different groups, there may be a real saving in the use of television for mathematics instruction. The major theories and concepts in a course might be presented on television by an expert lecturer, and the individual participation of students might be secured by scheduling small sections taught by teaching assistants, or by having a tutoring room available to all members of the course for several hours each day. This approach was reported successful at Washington University and Ohio State. Whatever place television may have in future mathematics instruction, it will certainly be more effective if the buildings in which it is used are designed for such a purpose. Certainly, conduits should be built in that are suitable for the coaxial cables used in closed circuit television. There should also be appropriate spots in classrooms where one or more television monitors (Fig. 66) may be mounted so that everyone in the class has a good view. Furthermore, there is need for a television studio

FIGURE 66 *Portable television receiver*

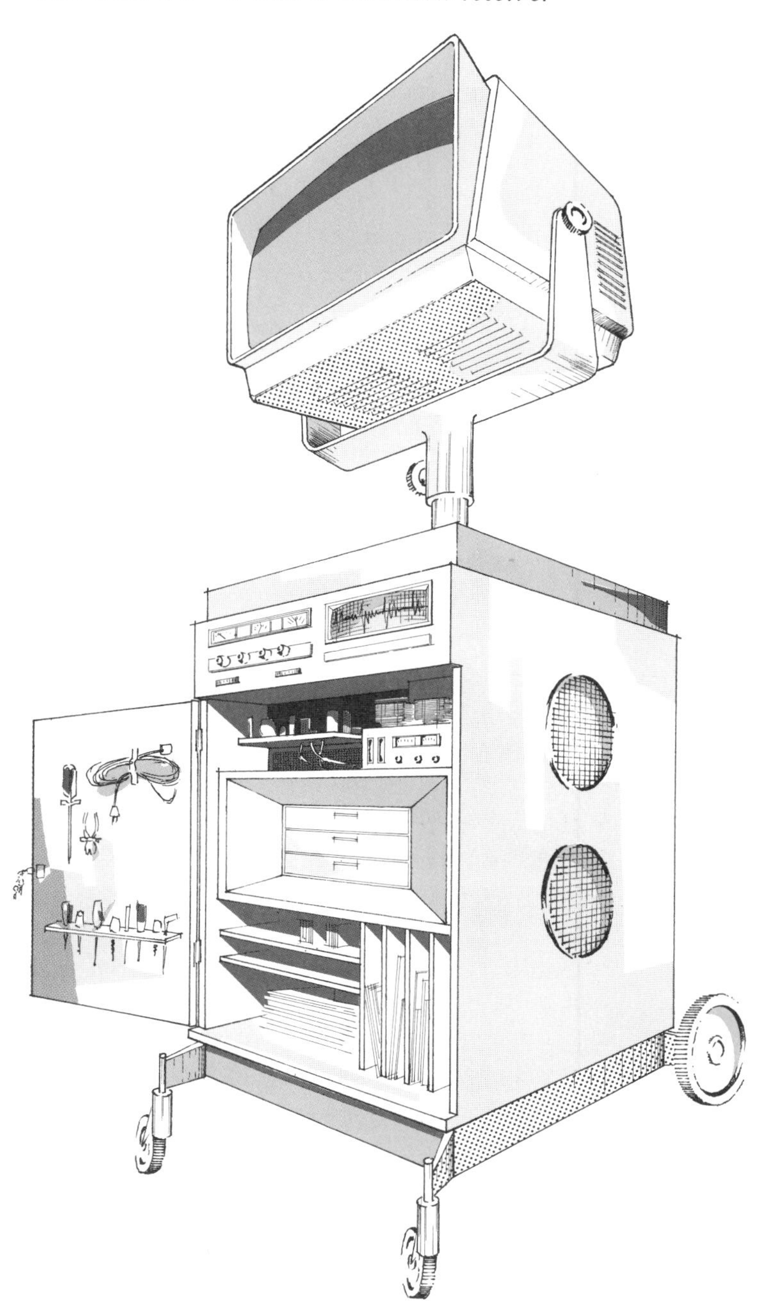

somewhere on the campus for broadcasting programs and preparing video tapes, and there is possibly a need for at least one classroom in the mathematics area in which a teacher holding a regular class could be televised for closed circuit television to be viewed in other rooms.

Mathematical instruction by television is already being tried out in many high schools; for example, in North Hagerstown, Maryland,[47] a number of mathematics courses are being given regularly by television, ranging from 7th grade mathematics to a calculus course for advanced placement. The television presentations are supplemented by discussion meetings with the classroom teacher. In some city high schools suffering from a shortage of qualified mathematics teachers, a master teacher may address several classes at once for 20 minutes on television and have his presentation followed up by questions and discussions under the direction of less experienced teachers in the several classrooms.

Television monitors, which are now commercially available, can serve only a limited audience of 25 to 35 viewers. Several monitors are needed to service a large lecture room. These need to be properly mounted for optimum viewing and require cable connections to be used for closed-circuit television. Whether or not television is being used in a school at the time the new building is planned, consideration should be given to the possibility of its future use, and the necessary conduits should be installed in the walls or floor when the building is built. Provision for darkening a room may also be desirable. Undoubtedly, the use of television instruction in mathematics will be greatly increased when the television industry develops a means of projecting the image onto a large screen that might cover the whole front wall of the classroom. Such a large-screen projection system, like Cinemascope in the movie industry, may come to television. If it becomes available for classroom instruction, it will have important implications for the design of classrooms. The need to see a large area at one time in learning mathematics suggests that some of the difficulties encountered (e.g., in television teaching) would be removed if slides were projected simultaneously with moving pictures on adjacent screens, or if films were made for large screen projection.

Models and other visual aids

A large variety of mathematical models are available commercially as visual aids for teaching mathematics at the high school or college level.[4] These include a variety of beautiful plastic models, string models, geometry boards, vector boards, and theorem demonstration boards. There are models of binomial expansions, conic sections, polyhedrons, and non-Euclidean surfaces. There are area models, circle models, and topology models. There are slated globes for teaching spherical geometry, linkages, demonstration measuring instruments, field instruments, and drawing instruments. There are models to illustrate important concepts in probability and statistics. In one of these, a normal distribution is obtained experimentally when several hundred small steel balls fall from a central hole at the top of the model through a lattice of nails that distribute the balls to the right and left into a number of vertical slots shown behind a glass cover. There are also probability kits and computer kits. Students interested in such activity may construct certain models and save the school the expense of their purchase. Such a project may be an aid in learning certain basic principles in mathematics, but should not be considered a substitute for learning mathematics. Mathematical models may be used simply for display purposes to excite the imagination and curiosity of the student, or they may be used as integral parts of classroom instruction. If mathematical models are to be used frequently in classroom instruction, some accessible place for their storage may be desirable. In certain high school classrooms, a panel of pegboard may be a convenient place for displaying models. Models are doubly useful if they are not only shown in class at the appropriate time, but also displayed permanently in suitable display cases. A model collection for display purposes only may conveniently be mounted in illuminated display cases inset in the corridor walls. A recently constructed display at the Museum of Science and Industry in Chicago contains many devices that could be used in mathematics department exhibits (Fig. 44).

Teaching machines and programed instruction

Enthusiasts for programed instruction call it a revolution in education of major proportions, with far-reaching implications for future patterns of instruction. The idea in one form of programed instruction is to present a body of knowledge in a short series of graded steps and to require an active response from each student at each step. The steps are each short enough that nearly all students are able to answer a majority of the questions correctly and are thus reinforced and rewarded by their correct answers.

The individualized instruction provided by programed instruction and teaching machines can be no better than the programs that are available. With good programs, they may well assist the teacher in imparting factual information, relieve him of some paper work, and leave him more time to discuss complex interrelationships and to stimulate creative thinking by his students.

There are already many devices, some simple and some quite complex, for implementing programed instruction. Some programs come in notebooks that only require a student to read a set of instructions, answer appropriate questions on what he has learned, check his answer, and move on to the next question. Such activities could be carried on in the seats of an ordinary classroom, but might be better accomplished in a setting where each student station has partial privacy.

More sophisticated methods of presenting programed instruction require the student to sit before a teaching machine, read one question at a time, and respond by pressing a button or making an electrical contact to indicate his choice among possible answers. The machine may include built-in devices to record the number of correct and incorrect responses and to time the student in his work. A still more elaborate device may project the questions visually onto an individual screen in a succession of frames and simultaneously present the same material through earphones connected to a recording. A room similar to a language laboratory would be appropriate for such machines.

Even more elaborate teaching machines controlled by computers are able to arrange the sequence of instructional units according to the responses of the student, allowing the quick learner to proceed rapidly at his own pace, but recycling the slow learner to additional instructions whenever repeated wrong answers show that he has not grasped certain fundamental concepts and needs additional drill. The future holds the possibility that a high-speed digital computer whose mechanical tutors are electrically connected to the computer's central nervous system may provide individual programing of the learning units to 10,000 or more students at once. If such individual programed instruction by machine is to be carried on in a high school, it will be necessary to provide rooms with individual student stations where the teaching machines can be installed and connected electrically to a computer on the same campus or elsewhere. The language laboratory suggests one way of meeting such a need. Space for individualized study may be an important feature in the mathematics facility of the future.[45]

SUMMARY

The explosive increase in mathematics enrollments recorded in the last seven years is expected to continue through the decade of the 1960's and result in mathematics enrollments in 1970 from two to three times as large as those in 1960. The increase is compounded by three factors: 1) the increased numbers of youth in the high school and college age groups (based on census data), 2) the increased percentage of the age group who complete high school and continue with their education, and 3) the increased percentage of students who elect work in the mathematical sciences. Demand for qualified persons with mathematical training exceeds the supply in teaching, government, and industry; at the higher levels of mathematical training, there is already a critical shortage, which is becoming more acute. Automation and space technology are accentuating the need for mathematical training.

Colleges and universities must move rapidly to supply the increased space required for instruction in mathematics, statistics, and computer technology. It is important that when these spaces are provided they should be well designed to serve the needs of college faculties that will use them. Appropriate spaces are needed for instruction in standard-sized classes, in large lecture sections for 100 or more, and in small seminars. These spaces should be designed to permit the most effective use of chalkboards, overhead projectors, visual aids, and possibly television. They should be well designed acoustically, well lighted, and air conditioned.

Spaces required for research include quiet, private offices for faculty, a departmental or divisional library close to the offices and adequately stocked with mathematical books and journals, general study rooms for undergraduates, and semiprivate study areas for advanced graduate students. Secretarial assistance to faculty members is an important factor in increasing their productivity as teachers and research workers; in a time of shortage of professional staff it is false economy not to provide secretaries and appropriate office space for their use. The administration of a large and growing department is a complex operation that requires well-planned administrative headquarters to make it smooth and efficient.

Computer facilities have sprung up so rapidly on campuses across the nation that a reasonable extrapolation of this growth indicates that more than half the college and university campuses in the United States will have a high-speed digital computer within five years after this is written. Although the majority may start as small installations, many will either start as major installations or will grow to that stature in a few years. Planning for computation centers must take this prodigious growth factor into account.

The planning of facilities for the mathematical sciences requires cooperative effort on the part of the mathematician, the administrator, and the architect. The department of mathematics or statistics should first make a careful analysis of its future space needs. It should estimate classroom needs on the basis of predicted enrollment trends;

calculate required office space for administration, secretarial assistance, teaching, and research; and provide for adequate library spaces, study areas, common room or colloquium room, preparation areas, and storage areas. If increased space is needed immediately, a well-documented request should be presented to the appropriate administrative authorities, who must decide among competing requests for available funds. After a request for new facilities for mathematics has received administrative approval, a departmental representative must continue to work closely with the architect and administration. He must make sure that none of the essential elements of an efficient facility is overlooked in adapting the specifications suggested by the department to the limitations enforced by the requirements of the site, the budget, fire and building regulations, and other boundary conditions with which the architect has to contend.

High school mathematics departments must also think through their space requirements in the light of new methods and techniques of instruction, including team teaching and visual aids, the increasing emphasis on individual projects and reading by students, and the need for teachers to grow professionally as well as to teach classes and work individually with their students.

The magnitude of the annual need for new instructional spaces is great already. It is estimated that, because of the peak birth rate in 1947, the overall need for new instructional space in 1965 will be nearly double the estimated need for new instructional space in 1964 and that this need will continue to increase in succeeding years. Planning for new instructional spaces must be begun immediately in many colleges, universities, and secondary schools in the United States. The mathematical sciences should be assured of their rightful share of these new facilities.

APPENDICES

APPENDIX A

Checklist of items to be considered in planning facilities for the mathematical sciences

APPENDIX B

Illustration Credits

APPENDIX C

Persons who attended the Washington Conference on the Design of Buildings and Facilities for the Mathematical Sciences, December 1961

APPENDIX A

Checklists of items to be considered in planning facilities for the mathematical sciences:

1. University Mathematics Department Spaces

Classrooms (standard- and medium-sized), some possibly divisible
Lecture halls (large and very large), possibly divisible
Statistical laboratory, equipped with desk calculators
Computation center (see details below)
Departmental library (see details below)
Undergraduate study rooms
Study areas for graduate students
Seminar rooms, possibly divisible
Lounge (or common room), with kitchenette
Colloquium room, possibly combined with lounge
Staff offices of varying sizes (see details below)
Offices for graduate assistants and teaching fellows
Secretarial offices (in addition to administrative headquarters)
Administrative headquarters (see details below)
Telephone and intercom or buzzer in each staff office
Storage closets for faculty use; major storage for departmental use
Display cases for models
Preparation areas for overhead-projector transparencies
Facilities for projection equipment (rear screen or front screen) and for television
Electrical outlets and conduits
Air conditioning and heating
Custodian's room
Location of elevator, stairs, corridor, toilets, parking areas
Room for expansion

2. Office of Mathematics Professor

Acoustical insulation
Lighting over desk and chalkboard
Appropriate heating, ventilation, and air conditioning (or fan)
Temperature controls
Telephone, with conveniently located outlet near desk
Electrical outlets, where needed
Electric wall clock
Panel of chalkboard
Panel of tackboard or pegboard
Shelving for books
Adequate storage for paper, reprints, and journals
Wardrobe closet or costumer
Wash basin
Venetian blinds
Executive desk
Swivel chair
Chairs for visitors (at least two)
Table
Typewriter stand, if needed
Dictaphone
Sofa, easy chair, or davenport
Carpeting
Door slot for return of papers

3. Mathematics Department Library

Adequate area (see p. 85)
Stack shelving for books and journals
Reading areas: tables and individual carrels
Reference areas, with abstracting journals
Card catalogue
Display shelves for current periodicals
Display of new books
Bulletin board, including current list of new books received
Current alphabetical list of periodicals received
Counter or desk for checking books in and out
Small conference rooms
Librarian's office and workroom
Copying equipment
Microfilm readers
Storage for microfilm and magnetic tape
Printer for magnetic tape
Information retrieval center and conduit to computation center
Audio-visual aids
Dumbwaiter
Room for expansion

4. University Mathematics Department Headquarters

Space for receptionist (with or without counter)
Office for department head, connected to reception area, preferably with private second entrance and private lavatory
Office for secretary, adjoining department chairman's office
Office for associate chairman, connected to main reception area
Offices for additional academic assistants
Offices for additional secretaries
Conference room adjoining or nearby
Workroom for duplicating equipment (with sink), adjoining secretarial office
Mail distribution facilities
Mail slots for paper graders
Dictating machine, typewriters, desk calculators, etc., for staff use
Textbook display shelves
Departmental reprint collection
Cubbyhole for student taking make-up examination
Telephone and intercom
Storage space for records, files, supplies, paper
Safe, or locking file, for examinations
Visual-aid preparation area

5. University Computation Center

Main machine room, possibly with elevated floor over recessed sub-floor
Observation area
Auxiliary machine room
Space for key-punch machines
Space for maintenance engineers
Space for mechanical equipment, including air-conditioning equipment and ducts
Temperature and humidity controls
Access for bringing in machines and supplies
Preparation rooms or "ready rooms"
Desk calculators
Conference rooms
Briefing room or classroom
Offices for director and other permanent staff
Offices for assistants and visitors
Telephone and intercom in offices
Space for receptionist and secretaries
Headquarters workroom for duplicating
Program library
Reference library
Lounge (or common room) and kitchenette
Good lighting and acoustics
Fire-fighting equipment
Custodian's closet
Storage for tapes, programs, records, paper, etc.
Card storage of the following types (those for current use must be under humidity control and the rest should be):
- a) bulk stock (area between loading dock and computer)
- b) current blank stock for punching
- c) codes and data under control of professional programmer, student, or faculty member
- d) permanent code decks (and their descriptions) controlled by librarian
- e) operational decks (at machine console)
- f) data files and extra code decks

6. High School Mathematics Department

Classrooms equipped with:
- (1) chalkboard, with map rail, and good quality chalk
- (2) lighting for student stations and for chalkboards
- (3) acoustical insulation
- (4) screens, stands, electrical outlets for overhead projectors, filmstrip and movie projectors, and conduits for television cables
- (5) seating and writing surfaces for students
- (6) desk and lectern for teacher
- (7) teacher's letter file
- (8) display and storage spaces
- (9) electric clock
- (10) intercom phone
- (11) panels of bulletin board or pegboard
- (12) wash basin
- (13) coat rack
- (14) pencil sharpener
- (15) wastebasket

Divisible classrooms for team teaching
Individual study and work areas, either in a separate mathematics laboratory, in the classrooms, or in the library
Space for desk calculators and possibly for a computer
Offices for chairman and secretary, and either separate offices or quiet work areas for teachers. Telephone and intercom
Conference rooms for teacher use
Shelving for book displays in classrooms, teachers' offices, and library

APPENDIX B *Illustration Credits*

Figure number

Cover: Dartmouth College Mathematics building, Hanover, New Hampshire. E. H. and M. K. Hunter, Architects.

Part I: John J. Flad and Associates, Architects and Engineers

Part II: Heavenly Clockwork, Joseph Needham, Wang Ling, and Derek J. Price, New York: Cambridge University Press; University of North Carolina Photo Laboratory (photo)

Part III: Fridley Senior High Photo Club, Minneapolis, Minn.

Part IV: Minnesota Mining and Manufacturing Company

1 Long-Range demand for scientific and technical personnel, National Science Foundation, NSF 61–65, Chart 5., p. 28
2 The Boeing Company, Seattle, Washington
3 The Boeing Company, Seattle, Washington
4 Aerospace Corporation, El Segundo, California
5 John J. Flad and Associates, Architects and Engineers
6 Universitäts bauleitung, Mainz
7a–14 McLeod and Ferrara, Architects
15, 43 Dartmouth College Photographic Bureau, Hanover, New Hampshire
16 Holloway-Reeves, Architects
17 Kistner, Wright, and Wright, Architects
18 Julius Shulman, Los Angeles, California
19 Jack Laxer, Venice, California
20, 22, 24, 26, 27, 30 McLeod and Ferrara, Architects
21 Walter Zick and Harris Sharp, Architects and Engineers, Case Studies of Educational Facilities, No. 4
23, 28, 31, 32 Schrader's Photo Shop, Princeton, New Jersey
25 W. Dobas, Ann Arbor, Michigan
33, 40 Hugh W. Celander, Photographer, Chicago
34, 38 Photographic Laboratory, Michigan State University
35 Arthur E. Princehorn, Oberlin, Ohio
36 Edward J. Schulte, Architect
37 Hammerschmidt Foto, Aarhus, Denmark
39, 42, 49, 53 McLeod and Ferrara, Architects
41 Luigi Pellettieri, New York City
44 Courtesy, Museum of Science and Industry
45 Town and Country Studio, Mt. Bolus, North Carolina
46 Walter Barnes Studio, Austin, Texas
47 Jessen, Jessen, Millhouse and Greeven, Architects
48 Claude Oakland, Architect, San Francisco, California
50, 63 Roland Quintero Studio, Palo Alto, California
51 Loring Studios, Boston, Massachusetts
52 Base Photo Branch, U.S.A.F.A., Colorado
54 Fridley Senior High Photo Club, Minneapolis 21, Minnesota
55 Bill Edwards Photography, Dallas, Texas
56, 57, 59 McLeod and Ferrara, Architects
58 Leon Lacabanne, University of Minnesota, Minneapolis, Minnesota
60, 61, 65, 66 McLeod and Ferrara, Architects
62 Minnesota Mining and Manufacturing Company
64 Newton (Mass.) Public Schools

APPENDIX C

Persons who attended the Washington Conference on the Design of Buildings and Facilities for the Mathematical Sciences, December 8–9, 1961

*Wallace Givens (Northwestern University); Chairman, Advisory Committee

PANEL A · ADMINISTRATION

*Carl B. Allendoerfer (University of Washington)
**George E. Hay (University of Michigan)
James A. Hummel (University of Maryland)
James Singer (Brooklyn College)

PANEL B · INSTRUCTION

*E. P. Vance (Oberlin College)
**Everett Pitcher (Lehigh University)
James B. Bartoo (Pennsylvania State University)
Jack R. Britton (University of Colorado)

PANEL C · STUDY AND RESEARCH

* Charles E. Rickart (Yale University)
**M. R. Hestenes (Institute for Defense Analyses)
L. J. Paige (University of California, Los Angeles)

PANEL D · COMPUTATION AND CONSULTATION

*George E. Nicholson, Jr. (University of North Carolina)
**David M. Young (University of Texas)
Robert J. Langle (Stanford University)
Arvid T. Lonseth (Oregon State University)

PANEL E · HIGH SCHOOL AND JUNIOR COLLEGE

*Donovan A. Johnson (University of Minnesota)
**Henry Swain (New Trier Township High School, Winnetka, Illinois)
**George Grossman (W. H. Taft High School, New York City)
**Aubrey W. Calvert (California State Department of Education, Los Angeles)
Emil J. Berger (St. Paul Public Schools)
Edwin C. Douglas (Taft School, Watertown, Connecticut)
*Sarah T. Herriot (Mrs. John G.) (Cubberley High School, Palo Alto, California)
Julius H. Hlavaty (DeWitt Clinton High School, New York City)
Paul W. Seagers (Indiana University)

OTHER PARTICIPANTS

J. Sutherland Frame, Michigan State University
Jonathan King, Educational Facilities Laboratories, Inc., New York
**John W. McLeod, Architect, Washington, D. C.
G. Baley Price, The University of Kansas
A. W. Tucker, Princeton University

INVITED OBSERVERS FROM WASHINGTON, D. C.

Richard A. Carrigan, National Science Foundation
James D. Gates, National Council of Teachers of Mathematics
Howard E. Page, National Science Foundation
Lauren G. Woodby, U.S. Office of Education

**These seven persons served as the advisory committee for the project. Six of them presided over conference or panel sessions. Those on Panels A, B, C, D, served as panel spokesmen for the recommendations presented to the conference. Emil Berger presented the recommendations of Panel E.*

***These eight persons presented invited addresses.*

BIBLIOGRAPHY

1 *American Standard Guide for School Lighting.* New York: Illuminating Engineering Society, 1962, see also: *Illuminating Engineering,* 1962, vol. 57, no. 4, 253–286.

2 *Architectural Catalog File, Sweet's Catalog.* New York: Service Division, F. W. Dodge Corporation.

3 BARTNICK, LAWRENCE P. *Designing the Mathematics Classroom.* Washington: National Council of Teachers of Mathematics, May 1957. Contains extensive bibliography.

4 BERGER, EMIL J., and JOHNSON, DONOVAN A. *A Guide to the Use and Procurement of Teaching Aids for Mathematics.* Washington: National Council of Teachers of Mathematics, 1959.

5 BOYD, D. K. *Blackboards and Bulletin Boards as Visual Aids in Education.* Pen Argyl, Pennsylvania: Natural Slate Blackboard Co., 1932.

6 BROWN, KENNETH E., and OBOURN, ELLSWORTH S. *Offerings and Enrollments in Science and Mathematics in Public High Schools 1958.* (Ser. OE-29021) Washington: U.S. Department of Health, Education, and Welfare, Office of Education, 1961. See especially p. 62.

7 *Bulletin no. 13, Provisional International Computation Centre.* Rome: Palazzo degli Uffici, Zona dell' E.U.R., 1961. Lists and describes European computation centers.

8 *Careers in Mathematics.* Washington: National Council of Teachers of Mathematics and National Academy of Sciences—National Research Council, 1961.

9 *Careers in Science, Mathematics, and Engineering;* A Selected Bibliography. (Ser. OE-26007, Bulletin no. 8). Washington: U.S. Department of Health, Education, and Welfare, Office of Education, 1961.

10 CHAPMAN, DAVE, and Staff. *Design for ETV—Planning for Schools with Television.* New York: Educational Facilities Laboratories, Inc., 1960.

11 *Committee on the Undergraduate Program in Mathematics, Annual Report 1961.* Michigan State University Oakland, Rochester, Michigan.

12 *A Comprehensive Bibliography on Higher Education.* Washington: Association for Higher Education, 1962. See p. 32.

13 *The Cost of a Schoolhouse.* New York: Educational Facilities Laboratories, Inc., 1960.

14 COWEN, PHILIP A. *Needs and Facilities in Higher Education in New York State.* Albany: State University of New York, 1957.

15 DEBERNADIS, AMO, and others. *Planning Schools for New Media.* Portland, Ore.: Portland State College, Division of Education, 1961.

16 *A Divisible Auditorium, Boulder City, Nevada.* New York: Educational Facilities Laboratories, Inc., 1962.

17 *Employment in Professional Mathematical Work in Industry and Government.* Report on a 1960 Survey, U. S. Department of Labor and Mathematical Association of America, NSF 62–12, 1962.

18 *Environmental Engineering for the School.* A Manual of Recommended Practice. (Ser. OE 21014) U. S. Department of Health, Education, and Welfare, 1961.

19 *Expansion, A Report on the Expansion of Boulder High School, Boulder, Colorado—a study undertaken at Boulder January 23, 1961–June 9, 1961.* Glenn A. Gilbert, Planning Director, Hobart D. Wagener, Architectural Consultant. See pages 15, 50.

20 *A Faculty Office Study: Design and Evaluation.* Pennsylvania State University, Division of Academic Research and Services and Department of Physical Plant Planning and Construction. New York: Educational Facilities Laboratories, Inc., 1961.

21 *Fifth Annual Survey of University Computing Activities.* Rochester, N. Y.: University of Rochester, Computing Center, 1961.

22 FLESHER, W. R. *Guide for Planning School Plants.* Nashville Tenn.: National Council on Schoolhouse Construction, George Peabody College for Teachers, 1953.

23 FRAME, J. S. *Solid Geometry.* New York: McGraw-Hill, 1948.

24 *Here They Learn.* First Annual Report. New York: Educational Facilities Laboratories, Inc., 1959.

25 *Horizontal and Vertical Circulation in University Instructional and Research Buildings.* New York: University Facilities Research Center and Educational Facilities Laboratories, Inc., 1961.

26 JOHNSON, D. A., and OLANDER, C. E. *How to Use Your Bulletin Board.* Washington: National Council of Teachers of Mathematics, 1953.

27 JONES, DONALD A. *Physical Facilities Analysis for Colleges and Universities: A Handbook of Techniques.* American Association of Colleges for Teacher Education, 1958.

28 LARGENT, FRANCIS D. *School Planning Laboratory Research, Report no. 2* (Transportable Classrooms). Stanford, California: Stanford University, School of Education, School Planning Laboratory, 1960.

29 LARSON, J. FREDERICK, and PALMER, ARCHIE M. *Architectural Planning of the American College.* McGraw-Hill, 1933.

30 LINDQUIST, CLARENCE B. "*Mathematics and Statistics Degrees During the Decade of the Fifties.*" *American Mathematical Monthly,* vol. 68, no. 7, Aug.–Sept., 1961. Also supplementary data from this author.

31 *The Long-Range Demand for Scientific and Technical Personnel; A Methodological Study.* National Science Foundation and U. S. Department of Labor, NSF 61–65, 1961.

32 *Mathematicians' Conference on the Support of Higher Education by the Federal Government.* Washington: Conference Board of Mathematical Sciences, 1960. See pp. 31–32.

33 MCLEOD and FERRARA. *Architects, A.I.A., Conventional Gymnasium vs. Geodesic Field House; A Comparative Study*

of High School Physical Education and Assembly Facilities. New York: Educational Facilities Laboratories, Inc., 1961.

34 Middlebrook, William T. *How to Estimate the Building Needs of a College or University; a Demonstration of Methods Developed at the University of Minnesota.* Minneapolis: University of Minnesota Press, 1958.

35 *New Schools for New Education; A report from Ann Arbor.* New York: Educational Facilities Laboratories, Inc., 1960.

36 *New Spaces for Learning: designing college facilities to utilize instructional aids and media.* Troy, N. Y.: Rensselaer Polytechnic Institute, School of Architecture, 1961.

37 *New Teaching Aids for the American Classroom, a symposium on the state of research in instructional television and tutorial machines.* Stanford, California: Stanford University, Institute for Communication Research, 1960.

38 *1962 NFPA Report.* National Fire Protection Association, 60 Batterymarch Street, Boston 10, Mass.

39 Palmer, R. R., and Rice, W. M. *Modern Physics Buildings.* New York: Reinhold, 1961.

40 Palmer, R. R., and Rice, W. M. "Laboratories & Classrooms for High School Physics; A Report of the American Institute of Physics' Project on Design of Physics Buildings." Reprinted from *Modern Physics Buildings—Design and Function.* New York: Educational Facilities Laboratories, Inc., 1961.

41 *Parking Programs for Universities.* University of Wisconsin, University Facilities Research Center. New York: Educational Facilities Laboratories, Inc., 1961.

42 *Planning America's School Buildings.* Washington, American Association of School Administrators, 1960.

43 *Plumbing Fixture Requirements in University Instructional and Research Buildings.* New York: University Facilities Research Center, and Educational Facilities Laboratories, Inc., 1961.

44 *Professional Opportunities in Mathematics.* A Publication of the Arnold Buffum Chace Fund. Buffalo, N. Y.: The Mathematical Association of America, Sept. 1961.

45 *Profiles of Significant Schools: High Schools 1962.* New York: Educational Facilities Laboratories, Inc., 1961. See especially pages 33, 49, 73.

46 *Profiles of Significant Schools—Newton South High School, Newton, Massachusetts.* New York: Educational Facilities Laboratories, Inc., 1960.

47 *Profiles of Significant Schools—North Hagerstown High School, Hagerstown, Maryland.* New York: Educational Facilities Laboratories, Inc., 1960.

48 *Profiles of Significant Schools—Schools for Team Teaching.* New York: Educational Facilities Laboratories, Inc., 1961.

49 *Profiles of Significant Schools—Wayland Senior High School, Wayland, Massachusetts.* New York: Educational Facilities Laboratories, Inc., 1960.

50 *Program for College Preparatory Mathematics.* Report of the Commission on Mathematics. New York: College Entrance Examination Board, 1959.

51 *Programs, '62. A Guide to Programed Instructional Materials.* (Ser. OE 34015). Compiled and Produced by Information Division, The Center for Programed Instruction, Inc., and U.S. Department of Health, Education, and Welfare, 1962.

52 *Project on Design of Physics Buildings; Selected Reprints of Articles on Physics Buildings.* Sponsored by The American Association of Physics Teachers and The American Institute of Physics. New York: American Institute of Physics, 1959.

53 *Report on a Conference of University Computing Center Directors, June 2 to 4, 1960.* Providence, R. I.: American Mathematical Society, August 1960.

54 Riker, Harold C., with Lopez, Frank G., College Students Live Here: A Study of College Housing. New York: Educational Facilities Laboratories, Inc., 1961. See p. 77.

55 Russell, John Dale, and James I. Doi. *Manual for Studies of Space Utilization in Colleges and Universities.* Athens, Ohio: American Association of Collegiate Registrars and Admissions Officers, Ohio University, 1957.

56 *Salaries Paid and Salary Practices in Universities, Colleges, and Junior Colleges, 1961-62.* National Education Association, Higher Education Series Research Report 1962-R2, 1962.

57 *Science and Mathematics in Public High Schools 1958* "Part 1, General Facilities and Equipment." (Ser. OE-29006) U. S. Department of Health, Education, and Welfare, Office of Education, Bull. 1960, no. 6.

58 *Statistical Handbook of Science Education.* (Ser. O–541339) Washington: National Science Foundation, NSF 60–13, 1960.

59 *A Survey of Research Potential and Training in the Mathematical Sciences.* University of Chicago, 1955.

60 *Teacher Supply and Demand in Public Schools, 1962.* Fifteenth Annual Survey, Research Division. National Education Association, Research Report 1962-R8, April 1962.

61 *Teacher Supply and Demand in Universities, Colleges, and Junior Colleges, 1959–60 and 1960–61.* Higher Education Series Research Report 1961-R12, Research Division, National Education Association, 1961. See pp. 21–23.

62 *Ten-Year Objectives in Education—Higher Education Staffing and Physical Facilities, 1960–61 through 1969–70.* Washington: Department of Health, Education, and Welfare, Office of Education, 1961.

63 *The Revolution in School Mathematics; A Challenge for Administrators and Teachers.* A Report of Regional Orientation Conferences in Mathematics. Washington: National Council of Teachers of Mathematics, 1961.

64 *The Things of Education; A Second Report.* New York: Educational Facilities Laboratories, Inc., 1961.

65 *The Uses of Television in Education.* Prepared in cooperation with the U. S. Office of Education. Chicago: North Central Association, University of Chicago, 1961.

66 *To Build Or Not To Build; A Report on the Utilization and Planning of Instructional Facilities in Small Colleges.* New York: Educational Facilities Laboratories, Inc., 1962. Based on Research by John X. Jamrich, Ruth Weinstock, editor.

67 WATSON, F. R. *Sound.* New York: Wiley, 1935. See pp. 140–144.

68 WEINSTOCK, RUTH. *Space and Dollars: An Urban University Expands.* A report on the economic physical expansion of urban universities based on a case study of the Drexel Institute of Technology. New York: Educational Facilities Laboratories, Inc., 1961.

69 WOODBY, LAUREN G., BARTNICK, LAWRENCE P., and CALVERT, AUBREY W. "Planning the Mathematics Classroom" *The American School Board Journal,* vol. 144, no. 5, May 1962. See p. 37.

INDEX